A LIFE IN CHAMELEONS

Selby Wynn Schwartz is the author of *After Sappho* (Galley Beggar Press), which was longlisted for the 2022 Booker Prize and shortlisted for both the 2023 Orwell Prize in Political Fiction and the 2023 James Tait Black Prize in Fiction. Her first book, *The Bodies of Others: Drag Dances and Their Afterlives* (University of Michigan Press), won the Sally Banes Prize from the American Society of Theatre Research.

The Bodies of Others:
Drag Dances and Their Afterlives

After Sappho

A Life in Chameleons

Chameleons

Selby Wynn Schwartz

REFLEX PRESS

First published in 2023 by Reflex Press
Abingdon, Oxfordshire, OX14 3SY
www.reflex.press

A CIP catalogue record of this book is
available from the British Library.

ISBN: 978-1-914114-07-6

1 3 5 7 9 10 8 6 4 2

Printed and bound in Great Britain
by Severn Print, Gloucestershire.

Cover image by matrioshka/Shutterstock.com

Fregoli travesti en danseuse execute une danse serpentine page 85.
© Institut Lumière. Courtesy of the Institut Lumière.
Lumière Vue N° 765 *La danse serpentine [I]*.

www.reflex.press/a-life-in-chameleons/

For my mother, who makes everything possible

CONTENTS

I. Fregoli the Chameleon

Il Camaleonte • Eden • Velia • The river Tevere • Roma
Termini • *Fregoli n° 1: Fregoli retroscena* • *Fregoli
n° 25: Segreto per vestirsi (con aiuto)* • Abyssinia • *Fregoli sa
vie et ses secrets*

II. Fregoli Backstage

Romolo the *sosia* • Romolo and Fregoli • Fregoli the
prestigiatore • Imitation Fregolis • Fregoli and Fregoli • The
sister of Fregoli • The story of the *servetta* • Backstage at the
Eden

III. Fregoli the Origin of Cinema

Cinema arriving in La Ciotat • Devices of the Lumière
brothers • Eponyms • The cinématographe v. the
kinetograph • Discarded devices • The cinématographe v.
Fregoli • The Fregoligraph • *Partie de cartes*

VII. The Future of Fregoli

Fregoli and the futurists • The futurists and the fascists •
Frizzo • Fremo • *Il treno delle 9,23* • One day as a lion •
Returning to Rome • *L'illustrazione fascista*

VIII. Fregoli in Eden

Marinetti moves forward • *Un intervallo* • *Fregoli
nº 2: Ermete Novelli legge il giornale* and *Fregoli nº 7: Sogno
nuovo* • Fregoli in Viareggio • The men of cinema in their
gardens • Fregoli in 1936

IX. Velia Remaining

Velia sewing • *Fregoli nº 9: Bagni di mare fine di secolo* • Santa
Maria in Via • A wife by train • Velia the *sarta* • Lenuccia
and the heroes • Villa Velia • Wardrobes • *Velia si sveglia* •
Finale Ligure • Velia in 1936 • Velia disappears • The
forwarding address of Signora Fregoli • Velia changing

I. Fregoli the Chameleon

1. Pregelj the Chameleon

Il Camaleonte

When Fregoli was born in Rome he was very short. It was 1867.

Rome has always been full of lizards. They are called *lucertole*, which has within it the word for light, just as lizards themselves do. Mostly they are *lucertole campestri*, lizards of the country, but they find in Rome the pleasure of sunlight on walls of cities destroyed a thousand years ago. There is nothing like a nice afternoon on the bones of a dead city.

The tail of a chameleon is two-fifths of its body and prehensile, like fingers. Chameleons can see in ultraviolet light. In general, the males are more ornamental. They have excellent eyesight and like to decorate things. One eye can be peering into a darkness so black it dooms all thought to desire while the other eye is looking around quizzically at the flower arrangements. It is not clear why anyone would have thought that a chameleon looked like a lion. But that is what they were called in Greek: lions on the ground.

It took Fregoli until 1889 to acquire the nickname *Il Camaleonte*. If only he could have rearranged the letters like hats, he could have been a *leone*, a lion stern and noble. But he was not the type to sit in front of libraries. He was a bright blur. He could lose two-fifths of himself and keep moving.

Eden

Fregoli left Rome for Livorno with one valise. In the valise he carried a moustache, a straw hat, a dress, a gentlemen's jacket, a lady's wig, and one pair of black pants so faded that they looked red under the stage lights. He doused them in water to darken them. He stood wet in the wings. He changed colour.

In Livorno the theatre was called Eden. It was a paradise of men with moustaches. But Fregoli, who had a bad cold, could hardly appreciate the other moustaches. He coughed in his dressing room.

Onstage, though, he was three thieves and a policeman. He was everywhere at once, in different hats. He was, in order of appearance, Elvira, her lover Enrico, her father Timoteo, the beautiful French ballerina Mimì, and a cook named Pasquale. There were no entrances and exits. No one ever touched anyone else onstage. There was only a glance, a blush, a bow.

After a show, Fregoli liked to be doubted. People wouldn't believe he was really Mimì.

IT IS ME ALWAYS ME ONLY ME

Velia

Velia was a girl he met in Livorno. She could sew. He married her.

When Velia was still a girl, Livorno was still a beautiful city. It was the sort of place Byron and Shelley wanted to go on vacation. There was electricity in the street lamps, and you could swim in the sea. The fascists hadn't occupied the theatres yet.

Shelley, who is well known for drowning in the sea, was trying to get home to Livorno, to Mary Shelley. But she outlived him. She stayed home in Villa Valsovano and wrote while he went sailing.

Fregoli was the kind of man who named his house after his wife. So Velia stayed put on a street in Asti. You always knew where Velia was. Velia had a fountain out front and gardens in back. He built his own private darkroom in Velia. She was, one biographer said, a veritable and proper castle. After a few years he sold Velia and went back to Rome.

Who knows what Velia thought? She had the second floor of the villa all to herself.

The river Tevere

Really all of Rome is a river interrupted by some fountains. As a child Fregoli lived between them. In his neighbourhood there was a great deal of *andirivieni*, which means coming and going at the same time. The good ones were going to Mass and the wary ones were eying the river, which overran its banks in 1870 and swamped all the fountains.

He was expelled from school and went to work for a watch-maker. But time bored him. When he realized that the sound of watches made time run more slowly, he left the watch-maker and became a waiter. Waiters could slip raw eggs into upturned hats and slyly stick moustaches to the wigs of certain ladies.

Fregoli liked a good tragedy now and then.

A river as grand as the Tevere is like a theatre or a train station. It makes people come and go in crowds, watching. At every moment there is a flow and a flux, arrivals and departures, entrances and exits, astonished surges of time forward to the breach. When Fregoli was younger, he would throw himself off a bridge into the river to see if anyone really loved him.

Roma Termini

In those days the pope ran the train station. It was called Roma Termini, not because it was the end of the line but because before this it had always been a bathhouse. For centuries the men of Rome had enjoyed its thermal steams together.

The pope quickly redecorated.

But after a few years the pope gave up. Ever since Rome had been invaded by the Italian Army, it wasn't the same. Every time you let the Italians in they would march around in their big boots, renaming the streets. They said it was about unification, but you could see where they were going with that. Back to the bathhouses.

Fregoli was too young to remember what the pope looked like. He was born in Rome before Italy existed. The Italian Army marched in their muddy boots through the *quartiere* of his childhood, renaming the streets. Wondrous he watched the stiff hats of generals go by. The soldiers splashed each other with water from the fountains.

The Italian Army took the train station but offered to let the pope keep the Vatican. With an injured look, the pope ceremoniously closed the door to Rome and withdrew to his innermost chambers. For fifty-nine years the pope never left his rooms.

They grew up together, Fregoli and the Kingdom of Italy, both lively and ungovernable. Rome was their capital, and Roma Termini was their point of departure. It was hot in the summers and infamous for the lateness of its trains, but from Roma Termini you could go anywhere. With a great gasp of smoke the train left the station, and *ecco*, there was Fregoli free in this new place called Italy.

Fregoli nº 1: Fregoli retroscena

Women were always giving Fregoli flowers. They were forever pinning white carnations to his jacket and telling him to remember them. *Addio! Addio!* Fregoli kept the flowers and left the women. It was easier to be sentimental about a white carnation than a blonde named Ernestina.

But the flowers looked good on camera. For example, Mr X comes into a drawing room holding a bouquet. A gentleman, he takes off his hat and proffers the flowers to the lady on the upholstered armchair. She is wearing a dark gown with lacy puffed shoulders like antimacassars for a sofa, and her hair is done up in a snood. You can tell she is a lady because she knows how to make that little moue when a gentleman offers her flowers. Their hands meet perfectly mid-screen.

The lady turns and bends down to place the flowers on the ornately carved table, and Mr X rubs his hands together in evident delight. This lady is a spectacle front and back. She is better than a sofa. She is worth the flowers.

But when he tries to kiss her, she makes a great scandalized O with her mouth. You can't kiss a lady like that with the door open. She wants this drawing room bolted, she wants the flowers locked in. Obediently Mr X rises and turns to fasten the double doors.

Actually, you should never turn your back on a lady.

In an instant the lady has cleaved her whole dress down the centre to her waist, splitting it open, and heaved it off camera. It is just one gesture, one quick torsion of the wrist, that rids a body of a dress. It can be done as lightly as waving goodbye.

Mr X turns back to find Fregoli in a bow tie that matches his own, barking with laughter on the upholstered armchair. All of the flowers have been in vain.

Mr X hates cinema.

Fregoli n° 25: Segreto per vestirsi (con aiuto)

Fregoli backstage was marvellous. He could take off his trousers with one hand while singing both parts of a duet. Yet twenty-three dressers went everywhere with him, peeling off his skirts as he ran past, snatching his hats as they fell. There was a dresser for the feathered fan and a dresser for the frock coat, a dresser for the false nose and a dresser for the ballerina slippers. He liked to have an audience in the front and an audience in the back.

Even when there was no time at all, Fregoli would pause in his bowler hat at the curtained door to the stage, turn back to the dressers, and make a splendid bow. He would stop time and take it into his own hands for that instant, the second it takes to be marvellous to your dressers.

When this became a film it was called *The Secret to Dressing Yourself (with Help)*.

Fregoli would show the whole film to an audience, and then he would show it backwards. How marvellous it was indeed to have a mobile swarm of men, constantly dressing and undressing him, swaddling and unbuttoning him, encircling him with their arms, holding his belts in their teeth.

Abyssinia

Once Fregoli went to war. He was frankly terrible at it. He didn't even know where Abyssinia was.

But once he got there, he was given a hat with a plume and a place in the barracks where rows upon rows of men reclined together.

In a city on the Red Sea, Fregoli looked at the regiments of unshaven men and saw ranks of future chorus girls. Immediately he set about getting them out of their uniforms.

But just before opening night the war cropped up again. Someone was supposed to go fight for the highlands. The plumed hats marched off, and Fregoli stayed behind, watching the ships steaming into the port. Now all by himself he would have to be the blonde soprano, the tenor with a guitar, the suggestible wife, the famous actress.

Of course he did it. He was a creature of impossible duets. He could condense himself and reduplicate. Ah, sighed the general, if only I could multiply my soldiers like this *camaleonte*.

Fregoli sa vie et ses secrets

Jean Nohain was a soldier in the French cavalry when he was young. He fought a bit on both sides, but when the time came he was there to liberate Paris. He took a bullet to the face for it. Thereafter on television he was always careful to turn his head to one side. He did various tricks on camera like that, sideways.

For example in 1968 Jean Nohain tried to take a snowman to New Caledonia live on television. Oblique, in profile, he watched while it melted into the sea. Then he went back to Paris, where the students had pulled up so many cobblestones that you could see the sand beneath them. *Sous les pavés, la plage!*

It was also in 1968 that Jean Nohain and his friend François Caradec published a biography of Fregoli called *Fregoli sa vie et ses secrets*.
But it was not his life.
And it told none of his secrets.
It was a book about only one person.

Fregoli of course had many lives, one right on top of the other. And so his biography could only be a scattering of scenes, a series of short films, a *court-métrage* of characters. In the antic traffic of everyone Fregoli became, in the overlapping of shawls on cravats on petticoats on a pair of black trousers faded to red, there was an *andirivieni* to rival any train station.

Live time ran so quickly through Fregoli that sometimes the film caught fire.

II. Fregoli Backstage

I Tregoli Backstage

Romolo the *sosia*

In every backstage with Fregoli since 1891 there had been Romolo Crescenzi. When Fregoli threw himself off a bridge you could be sure that Romolo was standing on the banks of the Tevere, watching.

Watching Fregoli was a full-time job, and Romolo did it discreetly for decades. Fregoli backstage would leave half the buttons undone. He would leave his dressing room wearing only a silk slip. In his hands whole bouquets of flowers would disappear.

It was Romolo who decided whether to let the cinematographers into the wings, Romolo who kept Fregoli in petticoats and rum. Romolo didn't go home again until 1913 when his mother was dying.

Romolo was a *sosia*, a double.
He was also, as they say, a dresser.
He was a modest shadow, but he put his fingers under the hem of everything.

Fregoli disappeared from his biographies any story of Romolo Crescenzi.
In fact Fregoli and Romolo for decades discreetly disappeared each other.
Together they had mastered the art of quick-change.

Romolo and Fregoli

Romolo was also the name of one of the twins who founded Rome. Those were the days when twins drank wolf milk and clung to each other at night.

Romolo Crescenzi had a brother, but even as a child in the evenings he sought out Fregoli. From their *quartiere* they would wander down to the river and watch the gas lamps being lit on the bridges. In the house of Fregoli his mother was dying of something no one could say. In the house of Romolo his father was lunging darkly through the rooms looking for something no one knew what.

The brother of Romolo was named Virgilio after the poet who wrote of the founding of Rome by a hero. Virgilio did not believe in wolves. He did not believe in twins. He believed in every man for himself, and he left the house soon after to go into business.

Fregoli was always a quick furtive creature. Romolo was entranced by the speed of his hands. In the dimness of the gaslight they interlaced their fingers and made strange animals.

Solemnly Romolo told Fregoli that he would cling to him like his own shadow. Fregoli laughed and said Romolo had better watch out, there wasn't a shadow in Rome could keep up with him, and he raced off over the bridge. But halfway across he stopped in a pool of lamplight, turned back to Romolo, and made a grand bow.

The main habitat of a chameleon is the centre of a circle of light.

Fregoli the *prestigiatore*

Fregoli and Romolo each with a steamer trunk under his knees set off for a theatre in Firenze. But upon arriving at the stage door, Fregoli narrowed his eyes. His white carnation froze in his buttonhole. A certain Bencivenni was getting up on stage and telling everyone that he was the true *Camaleonte*.

Very loudly and slowly Fregoli remarked to Romolo that Bencivenni couldn't manage a *Camaleonte* even if they blinded him like they do nightingales in Tuscany.

No historical trace remains of Bencivenni after that.

Those were the days before cinema. In live theatre in 1893 you could still disappear someone without raising too many suspicions. Maybe he was under one of the hats. Maybe he was with one of the dressers. Maybe he just got lost backstage. It's very dark back there, you know.

Before there was cinema, Fregoli was called a *prestigiatore*, an illusionist, a conjurer, a magician, an artist of permutable form, a triumphant smile and empty hands. A colour is red, and then it is black. A flower is there, and then it is gone. A woman twirls a parasol, and then she is a policeman scowling under his hat.

A *prestigiatore* can disappear his imitators or he can become them.

Imitation Fregolis

Dimitrio called himself *Dimitrio, il secondo Fregoli.*
Iris called herself The Mystic Chameleon.
Louis De La Fioure called himself Frégo, and Laurent Camby
called himself Frégoly.
There was one Fregolina who was seven years old and did
shows in Cesena.

There was Frizzo, Fremo, and Marylinn Lee.
There was Mademoiselle Fregoli and Signora Fregoli.
There was someone who called himself The Great Trickoli.
There was Bencivenni who was never heard from again.

There was The French Fregoli and The American Fregoli.
There were third and fourth Fregolis.
There was Miss Mudge.

Fregoli was not fond of his imitators.
But his solo *Il Camaleonte* was also an imitation.
It was the shadow of a solo called *Condensiamo* by the famous
actor Ermete Novelli.
And the solo of Ermete Novelli was an imitation of the famous
actress Eleonora Duse.
As Romolo would say, backstage a double is everywhere.

That is why a solo is never really alone.
We condense, we chorus, we reduplicate.

Fregoli and Fregoli

When Fregoli was a young man, Romolo laced him tightly into a nice blue dress. It was late in the evening. With blonde tresses twining around his shoulders, Fregoli knocked at the gate of his house, and the *portinaia* answered.

Fregoli asked to see Fregoli.

The *portinaia* stood barring the door and asked which, there was more than one in this house.

Fregoli blondly with an air of injured dignity said he wanted to see the father.

The father was on the fifth floor and opened the door at the third timid knock.

The blonde smoothed her nice blue dress with downcast eyes.

The father guessed immediately who she was and why.

At that hour of the evening, a girl in a nice dress, seeking the father of a young man, her sweet face streaked discreetly with tears! She could only be a *disgraziata*! Dishonoured by his scamp of a son! An innocent girl seduced and abandoned with child! The scoundrel, his son, good for nothing, *che scemo*, failed watchmaker, failed waiter, *che cretino*, now with his big dreams of the stage, *che idiota*, couldn't act his way out of a hole in the wall of Santa Maria in Via!

The blonde pressed a delicate hand to her forehead and fainted.

The father stormed into the kitchen for vinegar.

The blonde removed the wig, unlaced the dress, sat down on the divan, and calmly lit a cigarette.

The father stormed out of the kitchen with vinegar, muttering about sons.

Ebbene, babbo, said Fregoli to his father, offering him a cigarette from a little silver tin, you were saying, couldn't act his way out of a hole in what?

The sister of Fregoli

The sister of Fregoli was known to be a little rosebud of mystery.

It was said that the sister of Fregoli was immaculate, that the mere sight of a man in uniform brought a blush to her cheeks. The senators of the Ufficio Centrale took off their hats under her window. The *sarte* knelt at her feet to stitch her hems.

One evening in 1886 Fregoli and Romolo found themselves plied with prosecco by the venerable Senatore X, who wished only to know if the dear sweet sister of Fregoli might attend the masked ball to be given in a fortnight.

Peccato, said Fregoli, it's a pity, I would bring her myself if I weren't departing tomorrow.

Eh sì, echoed Romolo, it's too bad, *Senatore*, the sister of Fregoli loves a masked ball. And she's delicious in a lace mask, *bellissima*, a little mouthful of joy.

Senatore X pondered this dilemma with his tongue between his teeth.

In the end it was decided that the sister of Fregoli would be escorted by the honourable Romolo with the sharp-eyed assistance of two *sarte*. Thus on the appointed evening, the sister of Fregoli appeared enigmatic in a pale pink gown that suggested the innermost petals of innocent rosebuds. The *sarte* carried her elegant train with their needle-pricked fingers. The senators elbowed each other out of the way to dance with her.

Prizes were given for the Mystery of Beauty, and the sister of Fregoli, receiving second place, blushed under her lace mask.

At dawn ices were served in the private chambers of Senatore X, whose fingers were sore from being slapped by the sister of Fregoli. Romolo gripping a cufflink was restraining the Senatore from further improprieties. Though wilted at the edges, the lace mask of the sister of Fregoli was intact.
The *sarte* were yawning.
The sun was rising over Rome like a raw egg in the morning.
The honour of the sister of Fregoli was still as rosy as the dawn.

Senatore X was never to learn that Fregoli had no sisters.

The story of the *servetta*

Fregoli however did have a wife. Whenever a friend said to Fregoli, how's your wife Velia, it is Velia isn't it? Fregoli gave a broad smile and said that Velia was very well and in fact let me tell you a story about my wife Velia.

Well, Fregoli said, one day my wife Velia decided she needed a maid. You know wives, they can't manage a thing by themselves. So she got herself a girl, a little *servetta*, a nice girl, blonde. I was at the theatre all the time those days, hardly home at all, sent her a telegram in the afternoon saying I would dine with Jarro, you know my friend Jarro, writes for the *Pagine allegre*, and then I'd go straight to the theatre, no use expecting me. Velia settles in with her *servetta* for the evening, they're sewing and having a quiet tisane, and a fellow from the theatre comes pounding on the door all out of breath, saying, where's Fregoli, it's an hour to curtain and he's not in his dressing room, *che casino!* Velia sends the fellow to Jarro at once, maybe they're dining late, but Jarro says he hasn't seen Fregoli in a week, he's mystified, absolutely mystified, no dinner plans. Meanwhile Velia gets herself into a state, she can't think what could have happened, she's frantic with worry, she sends her new *servetta* down to the theatre to see if there's any news. At the theatre it's all chaos and confusion, *che casino! che bordello!* no one has any idea, Fregoli has disappeared, it's twenty till curtain, the *servetta* sits herself down in the wings to wait. All of the sudden, it's ten till, *che casino! che bordello! che macello!* there's a flash in the wings, and like lightning the *servetta* is at the door of the dressing room of Fregoli, the dressers are too stunned to stop her, in one leap she's inside, with one hand she's whipped off the blonde wig, with the other she's thrown off her apron and half her dress, of course it's Fregoli!

It's me always me only me!

I take a bow, gentleman, I do indeed take a bow, my dressers are applauding, it's marvellous, Jarro rushes in, Romolo is grinning like a wolf, in two minutes I dress myself for the first act, at curtain I am ready in the wings, I begin right on time with three thieves and a policeman, it's a marvellous story, Jarro writes it up for *Pagine allegre*, at the end you know Velia finds out and she says, oh no I liked that *servetta*, I'll never find another one like her.

Backstage at the Eden

Fregoli met Velia backstage in the Eden of Livorno where she was a *sarta* who kept to herself. Chiefly what people knew about Velia was that she could sew.
And now they knew the story about the *servetta*.

Many theatres were called Eden in those days. One of the most famous was the Eden of Milano, where the backstage was buried underground. The Eden of Milano was known as a haven of young actors. It was one of the places they went to become other people.

Fregoli remembered the Eden of Milano with affection from the spring of 1892, when he was young and sprightly and still doing three thieves and a policeman in the first act. Those were the days when Romolo would gamble with the stage-hands until he had enough for a bottle of wine.

From the Eden of Milano subterranean passages like tentacles went out under the seemingly solid *piazza*. Into the subsoil they burrowed until they reached the Teatro Olimpico on the other side.
Between the two theatres was a vast dark space of *andirivieni*.
In the rush, actors were mistaken for other actors.
In the dim corridors, actors became other actors.

Between an actor and his *sosia* there was always someone lingering backstage.
A man might disappear for weeks with his double.
A secret buried there might not surface for years.

The dressers collided and murmured their excuses. It was very dark, you know.

In any case, that Eden is gone now.

III. Fregoli the Origin of Cinema

Cinema arriving in La Ciotat

On the south coast of France a train is arriving in the station.
It is arriving right on time. It is 1895.
There are people watching the train arrive in the station at La Ciotat, but they are not in the train station. The train is a flat thing rushing out at them. It is arriving and it has already arrived. It is never arriving, or they would be crushed in their seats.
That is what cinema is.
It is a view and its double, a secret of moving without motion.
It is a forced perspective.

The train that arrives in the station of La Ciotat goes running from Marseille along the coast in blazing summer light, coming into towns where the boats are painted white and blue, passing little rocky beaches where people are peaceably bathing in the sea at the end of the century. The Lumière brothers would take that train whenever they came down to their summer villa in La Ciotat. In fact the villa lies halfway between the sea and the train station, and they owned not only all of that land but also the lovely view over the Gulf of Lecques. They owned vast gardens and a private dock with a boathouse from which they could row out onto the Gulf of Lecques and thereby regard with reversible pleasure the lovely view of their villa and its vast gardens.

The Lumière brothers made it a habit to own both views.
They also owned the factory where the views were manufactured.

They perhaps most famously owned the moment when cinema itself was first viewed, the moment when the workers were leaving the factory, and if the Lumière brothers so chose, they could run that moment backwards, watching their workers pause hapless as time reversed itself, and then, step by halting step, return to work, closing the doors of the factory in their own faces.

Devices of the Lumière brothers

The Lumière cinématographe was known as a reversible device. On the one hand it was a camera for taking pictures, and on the other hand it was a camera for giving the pictures back as flickering streams of light. The Lumière brothers liked to keep things neatly all in one place. In their summer villa in La Ciotat, they kept the gardener in the gardens. That way they could find him and film him without too much trouble.

The Lumière cinématographe had small claws.

In 1892 a cinématographe was patented by a man named Léon-Guillaume Bouly.
But in 1893 Bouly did not pay the fees for a second patent.
By late 1894, the rights to the word cinématographe floated as freely as a rowboat drifting in the Gulf of Lecques.

On the tides of 1895 what had been errant and free was guided securely into the private dock of the Lumière brothers, where it came to rest under the patent n° 245032. The Lumière brothers coolly paid the Bureau des Brevets d'Invention for fifteen years of invincible rights to the cinématographe. Then they went to lunch.

The Gulf of Lecques looked very tranquil, but there was a cold, cold undercurrent.

Eponyms

Lumière is the French word for light.

Much has been made of this. Less has been made of the shadows, which in French are called *ombres*.

Before there was cinema there was *ombramanie*, the art of shadows. *Ombramanie* was practiced by travelling magicians using nothing but their bare hands and a light.

The master of *ombramanie* was the travelling magician Félicien Trewey. In his hands shadows became the pompous silhouettes of politicians and the dark lines of soldiers marching to battle under drunken generals. Everyone came to see him mock the men of his time. He could dispose of entire regimes with one finger.

It seemed that almost as soon as Félicien Trewey met the Lumière brothers, he was having lunches with them. There were oysters, a chilled *chenin blanc*, congenial cigars. Carefully the Lumière brothers shook the hand of Félicien Trewey. Solicitously they pressed him to come again soon, to stay on for the weekend. They wanted to show him the lovely view. In the evening as the crepuscular shadows crept over the vast lawns of the summer villa at La Ciotat, the view was especially lovely. The fading of each day was like an era coming to its end.

At twilight when the lamps were being lighted, the Lumière brothers retired to the study to smoke their commendable cigars. The cigars made Félicien Trewey feel hazy at the edges.

The lamplight was soft, suggestive. Liqueurs were served in the study.

A sweet strange light green, chartreuse is both a cordial and a colour. Chartreuse is made by Carthusian monks in the Grand Chartreuse monastery in the Chartreuse mountains. It is an eponym, a thing called by the name of another thing. Its own name is transparent. It is also high in alcohol and glows a yellowy sort of green in the light.

Félicien Trewey awoke with a ringing hangover in the clear morning air of La Ciotat. The sea gleamed from his window, and he could not remember precisely how he had come to be in the employ of the Lumière brothers. But there was the flourish of the signature in his own hand. He would go to London on their behalf with a cinématographe. In his hands the cinématographe would conquer Great Britain.
The era of *ombramanie* entered its own twilight.

At lunch the next day the Lumière brothers made a toast to eponyms.

The cinématographe v. the kinetograph

In Italy before the Lumière brothers there was Filoteo Alberini. Filoteo Alberini was born the same year as Fregoli, and he too longed for celerity, fame, a century where people would stop dying of consumption and start inventing electric everythings.

Filoteo Alberini became a freemason and a great admirer of Thomas Edison. If it had a filament, he was a fan. So when Thomas Edison made a kinetoscope, Filoteo Alberini made a kinetograph. For once, he thought, he was in the right place at the right time. In his hands pictures would be set in motion. In Italy progress would at last lurch forward. He submitted the necessary forms to the ministry of industry and waited to be admired.

The ministry of industry in Italy moved slowly. Sometimes it ran backwards. There were alarming clicks emitted by its various offices. The forms received official numbers and elaborate stamps, or else they were inexplicably perforated and burnt up.

Months went by while Filoteo Alberini waited to become the Edison of Italy, the man of his age.

In the meantime the Lumière brothers breezily invented their cinématographe and had it patented in Lyon. In short order it had conquered the world. Then they went to lunch.

A year later the ministry of industry issued to Filoteo Alberini his useless patent, with a stamp in the shape of a sun splintering into a thousand shards of light.

Fregoli considered Filoteo Alberini a fine example of comic timing in early cinema.

Discarded devices

The Marvelous Electric Phantoscope.
The Eidoloscope, the Vitascope, the Folioscope, the Muto-scope.
The Zoetrope.
The Edison kinetoscope and the Alberini kinetograph.
Edison said there was no future in projecting films.
The Lumière brothers also said that cinema was an invention with no future.
But they patented it promptly anyway.

The Cinetographe, the Cinographoscope, the Chronopho-tographe, the Cinemacrophonograph.
The problem with all of them was that the flickering of images made people weep.
There was fear of the blindness that came from cinema, a con-dition called cinematophthalmia.

The Badizographe, virtually unheard of. The Lapiposcope, a doomed venture.
The vestigial Zoopraxiscope.
The implausible Aléthoscope.
The dubious Héliorama.

The Biographe. At least a whole life might be made in short film.

The cinématographe v. Fregoli

Cinema finally arrived in Italy two or three blocks from where Fregoli was born. From the doorway of his house if you went down to the Fountain of Trevi and took two lefts, there you were at the first screening of a Lumière cinématographe in all of Italy. It was March of 1896.

The street where cinema arrived in the *quartiere* was old and crowded with impoverished families, who lived on the lower floors with their children. One part of the street was formed by the wall of the church Santa Maria in Via, named for Santa Maria when she was on the way to somewhere else.
Actually the church Santa Maria in Via had been in exactly the same place since 955 AD.
Things in Italy did not always move at the speed they proclaimed.

In March of 1896, Fregoli was twenty-nine years old and multiplying himself across innumerable picture postcards. Each publicity photo was crowded with Fregolis because there were hundreds, and it was difficult to choose among them. The Fregolis jostled each other on the page. The demure French ballerina overlapped the daring serpentine dancer, the thieves rubbed up against the soldier, the tenor edged out half of the gardener, and the policeman almost drowned in the extravagant feathered hat of Mlle. Suzette.

In this month Fregoli was just returning from a tour to half of South America, and the twenty-three dressers were frantic with preparations for his debut in New York. In the meantime he was doing a few Mimìs in Madrid. He barely had time to visit the *quartiere*.

The cinématographe could take sixteen images per second, but Fregoli was already faster than that.

The Fregoligraph

Fregoli met the Lumière brothers in a theatre called the Célestins, the site of a former convent. He was giving some performances in Lyon on his way to Barcelona, and then one night in the first row there was Louis Lumière, watching him intently.

The Lumière brothers weren't above showing off for foreigners. They took Fregoli home for a month and gave him a tour of the factory. Fregoli was in every way affable and congenial, a gentleman in the drawing room and a quick study in the laboratory. He applauded emphatically each time they demonstrated a new device and exclaimed over the admirable precision of their diagrams. He befriended their elderly father Antoine, who was forever making mediocre oil paintings and telling the same story about that time he had met Thomas Edison in Paris. In the evenings Fregoli performed harmless little card tricks to amuse the family. He was seamlessly charming, everyone agreed, such a perfect guest that you quite forgot he was a foreigner.

At the end of the month the Lumière brothers had given him the Italian rights to their cinématographe for reasons they could no longer precisely recall. It is true that Fregoli moved with bewildering speed and, in the right light, looked just like a mercantile industrialist.

Fregoli took his new cinématographe back to Italy, made it run four times as long, and showed it backwards whenever he felt like it. He called it by his own name.

The Fregoligraph.
It sounded just like him.

Partie de cartes

As soon as Lumière brothers had laid eyes on Fregoli, they were struck by the desire to capture him on film. All month they stalked him with their cinématographe. Avidly they watched his hands darting through card tricks, his quick sharp flourish of a bow. One afternoon they found him at a table of men, his hands flashing as he dealt, the dapper white carnation winking in his buttonhole. He was irresistibly kinetic, and he laughed like a wolf at a waltz of the sheep.

Fregoli was in every way affable, charming, congenial. But he was also ruthlessly mutable. He was an irreproachable gentleman in the drawing room and an unabashed capitalist in foreign climes. With one eye he was gazing politely at a mediocre oil painting while with the other he swallowed the details of every diagram on the drawing board. He was a chameleon and a cardsharp.

It was rare that when Fregoli played a game with men he did not win.

After Fregoli the Lumière brothers never invited another foreigner home with them. They began to lock the doors to the factory when they went to lunch. But they kept the film of Fregoli at the card game in their catalogue, filed dourly under Lumière n° 764, *vue comique*.

Indeed Fregoli considered Lumière n° 764 another fine example of comic timing in early cinema.

IV. Fregoli the Magic of Cinema

Fregoli nº 14: Fregoli barbiere mago

Fregoli often said that if he hadn't been Fregoli he would have been a barber. Or a woman, Fregoli said, he had dresses enough to fill the wardrobes of ten women, but probably a barber.

The first thing about barbers is their fine strong hands. They take the whole head of a man into their hands and turn it about, looking at the angles, the lines. A barber is a man who knows what he is doing. He is a man who takes care of other men, and the other men just let him do it. How marvellous to let your head drop back into the dexterous hands of a man who knows.

The second thing about barbers is the way they cut.

In the hands of a good barber a whole jawline can change. A cheekbone is pulled into focus, and a profile becomes more leonine. With the sharp clean snap of a towel and the warmth of a leather strop, a man is given back ten years. A barber trims a bit, strokes the razor across the skin, tastefully obscures a gap, and there you have it, the clean straight line of a man.

It takes innumerable patient tiny cuts to make a new man.

When Fregoli made a film about being a barber he took great care with the cuts. The film was called *Fregoli barbiere*, but Fregoli himself called it *Fregoli barbiere mago* to remind people that barbers were magicians. In the film Fregoli the barber cuts the hair of a man, scissors and razor, strop and hot towel, until he has shaved down to the bare warm skin.

Fregoli takes out a watering can labelled *Brillantina Fregoli*.

He pours the watering can over the shaved head of the man in the barber chair.

The film jerks and falters for an instant. A sudden splice.

Then there is the man with a full head of hair again.

As Fregoli knew, the third thing about barbers is the magic of jump cuts.

Match cuts

What Fregoli liked about jump cuts is that they are a slight of hand done by film itself. With studied innocence they disappear a swatch of time and then look like nothing.

Match cuts by contrast are shameless changes made in front of everyone.
For example, Fregoli.
Fregoli on film was happening at top speed before your very eyes.

Around Fregoli a tornado of costumes took place. Clad in a frock coat with a frightful moustache, he was a conductor before his orchestra. Under his fine hands the music swelled, and then there was Fregoli curtseying in a ball gown with peals at his throat. In the glazed luminescence of the pearls there was something, you saw it shining, and then it was the bright button on the uniform of Fregoli the soldier saluting his captain. While you were watching the war in Abyssinia it became the war in Ethiopia. While you were watching the fading *fin de siècle* it became a new century, and suddenly everyone was wearing jaunty little hats.
It was vertiginous.
It was an unrepentant miracle of cinema.
It was a tumult of time, disguise, objects hurtling through the sky, distances abruptly abridged.

Watching a match cut, you hold desperately to one thing, because everything else is shifting around it. You find the eye of the storm on the screen. You hold the centre with your eye while the edges dissolve into chaos.

SONO IO SEMPRE IO SOLTANTO IO translated literally is *I AM I ALWAYS I ONLY I.*

In these moments you cling to the I.

Motion blur

Before cinema it was all slowness, calotype, and collodion.
To be photographed in the middle of the nineteenth century, you had to sit quite still. Favoured subjects were therefore those that had been dead for more than a thousand years. Preferably in ruins, they were visited and captured by avid foreign photographers. In Rome these images were called *vedute*, which were picturesque views of Italy falling apart.
There are many possible views on this.

Improvements were made to calotype.
Improvements were made to collodion.
Still, the lizards blurred the walls.

The actress Sarah Bernhardt could sit quite still before a photographer.
The photographer would fix her with a pensive look, her chin in her hand, her cheek to the light.
He would fix her with wet collodion. In his darkroom he would drip silver nitrate all over Sarah Bernhardt.
She remained pensive.
No one knows what Sarah Bernhardt thought in photographs because there were certain things that collodion could not capture. What women thought about, for example. Also, clouds. There are famously no clouds in the skies of the nineteenth century.

Fregoli in photographs could not sit still and be one person.

Therefore many Fregolis were always photographed at once. Trails of a body becoming its own ghost wafted across the collodion plate.

A haze of overlapping edges could not be fixed by any substance known to the nineteenth century.

Later this problem became a film effect known as motion blur. It was a technique beloved of the twentieth century which loved action above all, even bad action.

Fregoli of course didn't see why this effect wasn't simply called Fregoli.

After all, there was no shortage of him to name things after.

Titles of the works of Fregoli

Fregoli the barber, Fregoli the soldier, Fregoli that shy little schoolgirl from Sorrento.
Fregoli with empty hands and a triumphant smile.
Fregoli two, nine, and twenty-eight.
The only chameleon in Abyssinia.

Backstage, the serpentine dance.
In the wings, the spiderweb.
A card game among men. A joke about husbands. A night of love.
The secret to dressing yourself.

A new dream.
A serenade of Fregoli to
the famous actor Ermete Novelli who
is reading the newspaper in his garden.
Time for bathing in the sea at the end of the century.
Time for the train to depart at 9.23.

Fregoli after his own death, doing a show in Eden.
La mia storia, which means my history, my love affair, my alibi, my story, my biography, my lie.

Fregoli n° 28: Giochi di prestigio

When films first appeared they were very short.
Nothing could be cut because there was no time. Already each film flickered by so quickly that tears came to the eyes.

Just before the turn of the century Fregoli doubled the wheels of the cinématographe so that there was one on top and one underneath. When projecting, the cinématographe could be made to pass from the first reel to the second and then back to the top and then back to the bottom. With four reels a film could run fifty meters.

In this immense expanse of film Fregoli could do almost anything and undo it again. Flowers could appear in his hand. A tablecloth could fly off from underneath plates and glasses without disturbing them in the slightest. Water could be thrown out of a window and then stream back up again into its bucket. There was almost no need for a *sosia* like Romolo now that cinema could do its own doubling.

Finally there was time in cinema. Finally, as Fregoli said, there was time in cinema for magic!
He gave a grand wave, and colorized flowers burst out of his empty hands.
Immediately he made a film called *Giochi di prestigio*, magic tricks.

But others said darkly that the magic of cinema would disappear magic itself. For example Félicien Trewey damp in Britain knotted his scarf and mourned the end of *ombramanie*.

The future was whistling its way across Europe, urgent and sooty. It was a time of steamships and societies for the encouragement of national industries. The workers were leaving the factory and the cinematographers were patenting them. The citizens of many empires were flocking to demonstrations of the cinématographe.

The workers were leaving the factory, but they weren't getting very far. Only their images were moving forward. And in the great cities of fog and smoke, the shadows were waning. The yellow-grey fading of each day in London was like an era coming to its end.

Hawking cinema abroad Félicien Trewey grew old and successful and arthritic. He sent ledgers in his pained hand to the office of the Lumière brothers where they were filed away under *Trewey, F., Vue historique.*

There are many possible views on this.

Doppiaggio

In 1902 Fregoli had another idea about cinema. He would double himself and create sound in film.

First he made some chameleon films of himself.
Then he got a screen set up on stage to show the films.
The screen had cheerful coloured round light bulbs along its edges and said FREGOLI FREGOLI on all sides.
The cinématographe sat behind the audience rattling like a train through four reels of film.

Fregoli stood in the darkened wings, invisible. To each of his own characters appearing on the screen he added a matching voice. Mlle Suzette sang her *chansonettes excentriques* with a flirtatious quaver, the policeman bellowed out his warnings to the thieves, the thieves snickered and squabbled among themselves, the blonde soprano heaved great operatic sighs.
Miraculously the images opened their mouths, and words were heard in the theatre.

Decades later when synchronized sound was invented in cinema this was called *doppiaggio*, doubling, dubbing.
Fregoli just rolled his eyes.

IT IS ME ALWAYS ME ONLY ME

Cross-cuts

When Fregoli was in one place he was also usually somewhere else.

If he was entering stage left as a fetching brunette with a parasol, in no time at all he would enter stage right as a gentleman with an amorous carnation. Sometimes Romolo as his *sosia* would be the one hidden behind the parasol, showing just enough skirt to be believed. But often Fregoli would barely step onstage, his dressers pressing a gown against his chest like a false front, to say something fetchingly brunette. Then racing round to stage right to step into the silhouette of a waistcoat, he would tip his top hat to the coy parasol twirling on the other side.

That was live theatre for you. A lot of running around and pretending to be other people.

But with cinema you could pretend to be other people and not have to run around at all. With cross-cuts it was possible to interlace several scenes from different places while they happened at the same time. Whole stories were woven from cross-cuts.
Shot of the brunette with the parasol,
cross-cut,
shot of the gentleman plucking the carnation gallantly from his buttonhole,
cross-cut,
shot of the suspicious husband frowning.

Wholly different characters were made to seem related, and whole marriages were thereby ruined.

With cross-cuts there was no distance anymore between right here and over there.
Only in cinema could you have this breathless syncopation of entrances across continents.

V. Cross-Cuts Among Imitators

The *Serpentine Dance* of Loïe Fuller

In a cloud of pale silk in 1892 the dancer Loïe Fuller twirled and swayed on a bare stage in New York City. Under a patina of coloured lights the fabric flowed around her body in endless impossible flowers. Mesmerizing green became a blush of blue that bloomed into lavender and lilacs. She was a surface of layers in constant motion. She was the sinuous future of electric light.

Loïe Fuller called it her *Serpentine Dance*.

Borrowed light

In those days not everyone could have electric light at the same time. There was a general jostling for possession. To take the light for yourself was to cast someone else back into a century everyone was trying to leave behind.

Fregoli of course understood this. But he was a *prestigiatore*. He would take the light right out of your hands and you would never notice. In fact you would smile and applaud. *Bravo, bravo!*

In a theatre in Rio de Janeiro in 1896 Fregoli kissed the local municipal officials on both cheeks. He pumped their hands warmly. He signed their programs with a flourish and promised them extra tickets for the cousins of their wives.

The municipal officials of Rio de Janeiro issued a public declaration that at a certain hour of the evening, every tram in the city would stop running. Public transportation would come to a complete halt. The citizens of Rio de Janeiro would leave their suddenly immobile trams and peer up at the electric wires to see if there had been some kind of accident, a fire, some lightning. But it was only the declaration of the municipal officials that had paralyzed the city.

With a little wire, the officials had diverted the current from the municipal grid. The trams sat squat and abandoned in the dark. The little wire ran sparking with the current of the whole city to the theatre, where Fregoli needed all of the electricity he could get to become Loïe Fuller.

Cut to the *Danza serpentina* of Fregoli

And so in a theatre in Rio de Janeiro in 1896 Fregoli became
Loïe Fuller. To thunderous applause he twirled and swayed,
spiralling the fabric in endless impossible loops around his
body. He was a small body on a bare stage, but swaths of silk
floated everywhere around him, tinted by the lights.
He was magnificent and luminous and sold out every show.
He changed colours.

Fregoli called it his *Danza serpentina.*

Cut to the *Annabelle Serpentine Dance* of Edison

It was a long day in 1894, and Peerless Annabelle the dancer was tired. She was tired of skirt dancing. She was tired of the Follies. She was especially tired of Loïe Fuller.

Loïe Fuller was in Paris while Peerless Annabelle was stuck upstate in an airless box all afternoon with Edison adjusting his kinetograph. According to Edison, this place would be known to history as the first moving pictures production studio in all America. But everyone else knew it as the Black Maria because it was as dank as a paddy wagon, and hot.

Peerless Annabelle the dancer stood pale and resigned in the Black Maria.
The air was like tar, and the swaths of white silk drooped at her sides.
Edison adjusted his kinetograph.
The Black Maria began to turn.

Peerless Annabelle the dancer huddled limply under the hot lights. The Black Maria made her nauseous. It was like dancing in a coffin. Around her the dark walls trembled as they turned. Edison adjusted his kinetograph.

Peerless Anabelle the dancer wished that she were Loïe Fuller floating from one dinner party to the next. With a languid arm extended she imagined Loïe Fuller meeting the Queen of Romania. With a gracious turn she would accept a glass of champagne. Swaying she bowed before royalty. Twirling she descended the long staircase toward the upturned faces of her admirers.

Flowing about her the yards of pale fabric finally lifted themselves into the air.

Finally like the petals of flowers at night they bloomed open in the Black Maria.

At last Peerless Annabelle was dancing, bowing to the Queen, turning, floating, late at night, her admirers, twirling, the flowers, the champagne, swaying, spiralling, everywhere at once, becoming everyone, becoming and turning away, inimitable, electric, peerless, breathless.

Edison called his film *Annabelle Serpentine Dance*.

Peerless Annabelle the dancer called her mother and said she had a terrible headache.

Loïe Fuller in Paris called her lawyer and asked sharply what was the name of that girl.

At that time Loïe Fuller in Paris

No one ever succeeded in making a film of Loïe Fuller performing her *Serpentine Dance*.

Many attempts were made with kinetoscopes and cinématographs and elaborate lunches with champagne, but Loïe Fuller didn't like film. More precisely she didn't trust film. She told her girlfriend Gab that she wouldn't be caught dead in a Black Maria with a man like Edison. Loïe Fuller was no fool. She was from just outside Chicago. Her real name was Mary Louise. She stayed in Paris where she could be appreciated properly and people clamoured to paint her portrait.

In Paris at that time the Queen of Romania was nodding sympathetically over a teacup. Fanning herself with great feeling Loïe Fuller sighed and said again that a true artist is always alone in her art. *Mais oui*, said the Queen, it could be no one but you, the Serpentine dance, *ma chère Lo*, it is always you, only you.

Loïe Fuller in Paris snapped her fan shut and muttered to Gab that her next piece was damn well going to be *Copyright Law Dance*.

Yet the *Annabelle Butterfly Dance* of Edison

Coolly from Paris Loïe Fuller began to press charges against a number of her imitators.
Edison was undaunted, but it all gave Peerless Anabelle a terrible headache.

Edison got Peerless Annabelle back in the Black Maria and said, look kid, just pretend you're a butterfly.

Peerless Annabelle the dancer gave Edison a murderous wilted butterfly look.
The Black Maria began to turn.

The *Annabelle Butterfly Dance* had to be edited very carefully before its release to the American public.

Frames

Meanwhile the Lumière brothers boarded the first-class car of
a train bound south, looking for a dancer of their own. They
supposed that if you kept a gardener in the garden then nat-
urally you kept a *danse serpentine* in Rome where it was hot
and reptilian. The china rattled as the views rolled by, frame
by window frame. There was a screech when they crossed the
border into Italy, and it seemed to the Lumière brothers that
everything slowed,
the train, the views, the teapot pouring into the china cups.
The afternoon itself was hardly crawling forward.
By the time they reached Rome
there was such a delay
that each moment
had gone down to
sixteen frames
per second.

Meanwhile in Rome

In Rome the Lumière brothers set about sending hothouse bouquets to the hotel room of the dancer Teresina Negri. In photographs Teresina Negri was lithe and comely with curious eyes that were bright and dark at the same time. Notes of admiration for the artistry of Teresina Negri, the vision, the grace, really the inimitable presence of Teresina Negri, were pinned through the stems of the roses. With the greatest respect the Lumière brothers wished only to praise her artistry, which they found so singular, so spiritual, peerless really.

Teresina Negri in an extravagant scrawl replied of course it would be a pleasure, an honour, to lunch with the gentlemen of the cinématographe, but when, it was not certain. A theatre of Napoli, so difficult, pursuing her always, they must understand how she trembled before the theatre of Napoli, and then Anna Pavlova arriving now in Monaco, ah, to drown to death in the dancing of Pavlova! But for the roses a thousand gratitudes to the gentlemen, so rare to find among men of the world this sincere appreciation for the true artist.

Teresina Negri on a train again somewhere closed her bright dark eyes and slept until Monaco.

Limoncello

In the absence of Teresina Negri the Lumière brothers set about waiting in Rome. They waxed their moustaches and polished their glasses and had two fine suits made of Italian wool. One day the morning papers announced that Teresina Negri had been seen dallying in Monaco on the arm of a certain young viscount. There were pictures.

The Lumière brothers put on their new wool suits and went to the theatre to find another dancer.

At the theatre that night was a *Danza serpentina*. There was the twirling and the swaying, the swaths of fabric floating everywhere like flowers. The Lumière brothers felt quite mesmerized by the green as it became a blush of blue blooming into lavender and lilacs. Also the Italian liqueurs made your head spin. The *limoncello* in particular was a vile shade of yellow and smelled like surgical spirits.

With some delay the next morning the Lumière brothers roused themselves and set about sending bouquets of flowers to the dressing room of their new dancer. But they kept the curtains in their hotel room closed as the glaring sunlight of Rome gave them terrible headaches.

La danse serpentine of the Lumière brothers

In surprisingly short order the Lumière brothers had secured an agreement with their new dancer for a film of *La danse serpentine*. They had barely sent her any roses at all, and she demurely refused the offer of lunch at their expense. Such modesty was becoming in a woman of the stage, the Lumière brothers said to each other. So often these actresses went around imperiously as if they were the only ones in the world. As if they were not merely minor moving parts in a much larger machine, replaceable when they wore out. When something got ragged after a time under the claws of the Lumière cinématographe, they simply manufactured a new one. It was very convenient. It was why they owned the factory.

On a bare stage in Rome the Lumière brothers waited for their new dancer to finish dressing. At last she appeared, her body small under the swaths of pale fabric, and began dancing.

She was deliciously light, quick, each gesture draped on the air, a luminous form hovering between the waves of fabric surging around her. She was a creature half-flower and half-*meduse*, the Lumière brothers murmured to each other, an undersea jellyfish blooming into light. She twirled and swayed for them all afternoon, sinuous and electric, constantly in motion, tirelessly serpentine.

The Lumière brothers called the film *La danse serpentine, Lumière vue n° 765.*
Fregoli called the film A joke about the Lumière brothers.
La mia danza serpentina, la mia storia!

Condensiamo

Over limoncello that night Fregoli laughed uproariously with his twenty-three dressers. By the end of the bottle *Lumière vue n° 765* had acquired hundreds of new names.

A joke about women and snakes! A joke about women of the stage! *Condensiamo!* Medusa in person! Don't touch the serpent! Don't get lost backstage, it's very light back there! Lots of love, Loïe! How many chameleons does it take to change a lightbulb? Don't worry they're all Italians! Don't worry it's all the same dress!

A *prestigiatore* can disappear his imitators, or he can become them.

IT IS ME ALWAYS ME ONLY ME
Fregoli pinned the note through the stem of a rose and sent it to the Lumière brothers.

Excerpt from the Catalogue Lumière,
vue n° 765, *La danse serpentine [I]*

(Fregoli travesti en danseuse execute une danse serpentine.)

This film is a travesty, the Catalogue Lumière reports, this whole Fregoli is a travesty.

Well Fregoli liked a good travesty now and then.

Still in Rome

The Lumière brothers lowered the brims of their hats against the garish sunlight of Rome. They brooded abstemiously in their hotel room. They cleaned the little claws of their ciné-matographe.

On the fine stationery of their hotel certain letters were sent post-haste to Monaco. The next week Teresina Negri came flitting back to Rome like a surprised butterfly.

As it happened the Lumière brothers were quite free then and would like nothing better than to invite the distinguished Mademoiselle Negri to lunch. Perhaps she could bring her serpentine dress. They would so very much like to admire her dress under the lights.

As it happened they had the lights all ready.

La danse serpentine II of the Lumière brothers

The true artist is one always ready in spirit, Teresina Negri said to her maid. So we must rise to meet each moment, beautiful, like a bird.

After lunch Teresina Negri a bit heady with champagne changed into her serpentine dress. The Lumière brothers murmured their praises and adjusted the lights to bathe her in lavender, in lilac, in a chilled chartreuse, in a red as lavish as hothouse roses.

Teresina Negri was poised to take flight, she was a swallow darting and swooping over the river Tevere at twilight, she was a butterfly trembling upon the edge of a moment that only comes once.
Solemnly she decided that she would perform her famous solo for them.
Yes of course they could film if they wanted, it was nothing to her.

The Lumière brothers with grim satisfaction called their film *La danse serpentine II, Lumière vue n° 765.1*. At least now they had two of them.

Il Messaggero

Teresina Negri from the silken depths of her bed rang for her maid. The roses were wilting, and she could not bear the sight of their petals fading, the leathery leaching of colour. They must be thrown out at once.

The maid took out the ageing roses and brought in the morning papers. Teresina Negri paging through *Il Messaggero* gave a sudden piercing cry.
She was there on the page.
It was announced that in the next Lumière film the famous solo of Loïe Fuller would be attempted by lithe little Teresina Negri. Dubiously it was considered, the likes of Teresina Negri undertaking the legendary dance of La Loïe. And swiftly it was concluded by this messenger, this harbinger, this bearer of fates, that her slight charms were already waning.

Teresina Negri felt herself pinned to the third page of *Il Messaggero*. She could not bear to look, but weakly she looked. There were pictures, a row of pictures with names, like specimens of dead things in a book.

Cross-cut back to Loïe Fuller in Paris

Inexorably from Paris Loïe Fuller pressed charges against a number of her imitators. As she said with a sigh to her girl-friend Gab, as soon as you get one of them there's another one right behind her.

Cutaway to Gab Sorère

Gab Sorère the girlfriend of Loïe Fuller was sixteen years younger. Gab wore smart suits and had a slightly crooked smile. Almost no one could get Gertrude Stein to play poker, but Gab could.

For many years Gab and Lo lived together in Paris. Sometimes Lo compared Gab to velvet. At other times Lo compared Gab to a young adder. When someone asked Lo about Gab, she would say, oh Gab I adore her, she's like velvet, actually you know she's all bite no hiss.

Lo knew what she wanted, and generally she got it. She got patents for her lantern projectors, and she got injunctions for her imitators. She got an invitation to the house of Marie and Pierre Curie where she got them to give her some radium. It made mysterious phosphorescent streaks on her dresses.

Radiant and stubborn Lo lived with Gab until 1928 when she died.
Then Gab Sorère put on a black suit with a black tie and reading their old letters wept in the study with the doors bolted.

Sententiously the papers began their proclamations of the legacy of Loïe Fuller.
Jean Cocteau the avant-garde filmmaker said that Loïe Fuller created the phantom of an era.
Marinetti the futurist said that Loïe Fuller achieved the metallicity of the futurist dance.

Rimbaud the poet said that Loïe Fuller was a sign that poetry will give rhythm to action in advance.

Mallarmé the symbolist said that Loïe Fuller was always a symbol, never a someone. In fact, Mallarmé went on, Loïe Fuller was not a woman who danced because she was not really a woman, but rather a metaphor.

Gab Sorère thought Mallarmé deserved to be bitten in the foot by the metaphor of a venomous adder.

She thought that if anyone was going to say what Loïe Fuller had been it should be someone who loved her radiant and stubborn, a woman. It took years after the death of Lo before Gab could stand to look at a camera. But finally Gab made a film for Lo, all in black light so the dancers would shine in the dark.

VI. Women in the Life of Fregoli

Fregoli among women

There are very few women in the life of Fregoli except for the ones he was himself.

He liked women well enough. He liked their ringlet curls and the stiff stays of their corsets, he liked the bright trickle of their voices filling up a drawing room, he liked the flash of their clever hands as they stitched. Fregoli thought that women were a fine thing indeed.

Women were also on the whole a better joke than men were.

To appear as a man you had to be something.
To appear as a woman you simply appeared in a dress.
Then everyone laughed.

That was why Fregoli could enter stage left as a brunette, a fetching brunette and nothing more, but then racing round to stage right he had to become a particular jealous husband. Or an amorous gentleman whose intentions were as plain as Senatore X in the raw light of morning. Or a waiter, a thief, a gardener, a barber, a policeman, a soldier, the famous actor Ermete Novelli.
Whereas if you were a woman you were always only a creature in a dress.

Oh Fregoli admitted that it was possible to be some other animal, if you were a woman. There were always butterflies. Or you could be a serpent.

Furthermore Fregoli felt that women were very good in stories. There was the marvellous one about the *servetta* of Velia. There was the Brazilian heiress who had awaited him in her snow-white carriage pulled by four coffee-coloured mules, there was the ethereal Parisian Liane de Pougy who had sent him perfumed letters. There were all of the white carnation girls and some red ones too.

The only problem with women really was that when you were among them there was nothing more to say, they had already got the joke about women.

Women of the theatre

Fregoli aspired therefore to be among only the most dazzling women of the theatre. He adored the distant stars in their firmament of stage lights. He wanted to sit at the feet of actresses as severe as icons of the Madonna, serene in their silence. He worshipped Sarah Bernhardt and Eleonora Duse.
The Divine Sarah.
La Duse.

If only he could become Sarah Bernhardt who was always herself at every moment. Sarah Bernhardt was like a collodion sky. The roles came over her, she became Hamlet one day and the Lady of the Camellias the next, but she remained cloudless and clear. A photograph of the Divine Sarah was an image of an actress at rest. She could stay very still and think about things.

But then also if only he could become Eleonora Duse who sank utterly into each role and was devoured by it. Standing in the wings to feel a hot breath behind you, needled teeth on your skin, to be deliciously eaten alive every night on stage. La Duse never doubted. She was only ever one thing at a time. She never thought about her characters because she was always gone when they came. She left herself empty, and they devoured her emptiness.

Eleonora Duse never went to the theatre unless she was the one onstage. As she said to her girlfriend Lina Poletti, actresses are exhausting, they always ask you what you think.

When Fregoli went to the theatre he saw the forms of the Divine Sarah and La Duse from far away, glittering like icy constellations. He sent reverent notes to the stage door with sprays of star-gazing lilies. He kept their likenesses tucked into the frame of his dressing room mirror. But he never asked either of them what they thought about.

Sarah Bernhardt v. Eleonora Duse

Of course they disliked each other.

Everyone said about Sarah Bernhardt that she was always and irremediably herself. You could see her showing through the characters like a bright slip under a dress. The only part you couldn't see was what she really thought about.

Whereas everyone said about Eleonora Duse that she was a raw material. When exported beyond the stage door she was inchoate and hypochondriac. But in each role, she became someone else. When her hand trembled on the doorknob of *A Doll's House* it was Nora's hand.

Sarah Bernhardt was French, and Eleonora Duse was born in a third-class train car near Pavia somewhere. Sarah Bernhardt had unfathomable dark eyes and kept a lion cub in her flat in Paris. It was widely rumoured that Sarah Bernhardt slept in a coffin. She smiled and said that it helped her to get into character.

As Eleonora Duse said to her girlfriend Lina Poletti, actresses are so tiresome, they always want you to believe them.

Tristano Somnians

Lina Poletti had a tolerant smile reserved for what Eleonora Duse said. Lina Poletti thought actresses were not tiresome at all.
Lina Poletti liked women onstage, and she liked women backstage.
Lina Poletti in fact never got bored of other women.

In the early days a note from Lina Poletti would arrive at the stage door signed *Tristano Somnians*.
Tristano is the man who puts his head in the lap of Isolda.
Somnians is the gerund for dreaming.

Everyone knew it was perilous to have an *aperitivo* with Lina Poletti. She wore a rosebud in her buttonhole and kept her hands purposefully out of the picture. She never signed her letters with her own name. But even Eleonora Duse who despised the taste of vermouth could not resist an *aperitivo* with Lina Poletti.

With a bitterness on her tongue Eleonora Duse declared to Lina Poletti, no actress should exist offstage, they should all perish on the sill of the stage door and be buried under the gaslights.
Lina Poletti smiled into her glass.
Fine then, La Duse offstage did not exist. But Lina Poletti did.

All that week Lina Poletti wondered whether Eleonora Duse was herself in bed or whether she was other women.
There was really only one way to find out.

Lina Poletti straightened her collar and went to the theatre.

Eleonora Duse might not exist offstage, but feverish in her bed she dreamt she was Isolda.

The menagerie of Sarah Bernhardt

In the time of Sarah Bernhardt to be an actress was to surround yourself with animals. The men who ran the theatres had gleaming teeth and tried to convince you to sign things in smoky rooms. The men who ran the cinématographe would polish its little claws right before your scene.

In the mornings Sarah Bernhardt rose refreshed from her coffin and yawned a beautiful silent howl.
From a bowl on the balcony her lion cub had breakfast.
Together they looked out over the wilderness that was Paris.

On a jewelled leash Sarah Bernhardt walked her crocodile in the Jardin du Luxembourg.
The photographers seemed to be hiding behind every tree.
They went lunging and snapping at Sarah Bernhardt.
As she pointed out, this made her crocodile nervous.

In 1915 Sarah Bernhardt had one leg amputated. Still she was relentlessly herself. She sat right down on the stage and did her roles in a chair. Backstage one-legged she was carried to her dressing room where at least one small grey wolf awaited her, maybe two.

Fregoli and the Divine Sarah

Fregoli met Sarah Bernhardt in Paris in 1900 when the Théâtre Trianon had just burnt down with half his wigs in it. While Romolo was visiting every horsehair merchant in the Marais, Fregoli contrived to call on the Divine Sarah with a cage of exotic birds under one arm.

She regarded him severely.

Fregoli became pale and small and stammered about the brightness of birds.

I know it was your fire lizards, wasn't it, said the Divine Sarah to Fregoli, you can't bring them backstage, they're a terrible nuisance and they'll burn the whole place down if you let them.

Fregoli with great wide eyes nodded mutely.

In 1916 Sarah Bernhardt had a theatre in Paris named after her. She invited Fregoli to perform in it and he came back all the way from Cuba dodging German submarines to say yes. It was the war, but Fregoli never denied the Divine Sarah.

After the show Fregoli looked up at the Divine Sarah sitting in the centre of the empty house and saw her spectral, seventy-two, pale from the blackouts and tinned rations. But still Fregoli saw such fire in her that she burnt up all the light around her.

Houselights would never dim the Divine Sarah.

Cinema and its lackeys could come and go, it was all the same to her.

In her lap a peacock blazed.

In her old age the Divine Sarah disdained the idea of dissolving her menagerie.
She refused the offer of a celluloid prothesis.
She would die in Paris in the midst of her own film, her hands buried in fur.

The death of La Duse

Eleonora Duse used to say that without the stage she would die. She would gasp like a fish through anguished gills, and her heart would simply shudder to a stop. The dank air of dressing rooms and the dim flicker of gas jets were to her the sun, the moon, the only place she could breathe without that strange sharp pain in her chest. She was a creature of the stage.

In 1898 Eleonora Duse came to Rome to star in a play called *Dream of a morning in spring*. The amorous poet who had written the play for her in fact slept dreamlessly every night, and then one spring became a fascist. But at that time it was still 1898 in Rome. The poets were not yet fascists, and in those days they wanted only to sleep with La Duse.

In her dressing room Eleonora Duse accepted the lilies from Fregoli with a melancholy air.
Ah, La Duse said to Fregoli, perhaps he would understand, the name of her death was cinema.
In the eyes of La Duse cinema should be known as the death of all women of the stage.

But Eleonora Duse knew that Sarah Bernhardt would betray her. Eleonora Duse was younger, but she had ordinary rather plain eyes instead of the dark unfathomable ones favoured by photographers. Also Eleonora Duse had been born in a third-class train car in the provinces somewhere which she never forgot. It was the fate of Eleonora Duse to die in Pittsburgh.

Before her death she cursed Sarah Bernhardt for giving in to cinema. Ah Sarah, with your lions and your coffins, not so divine after all under the hard lights of film, they will all see you mortal at last, celluloid impressions of your waning years will be wrapped up in metal cans and kept.

In 1916 Eleonora Duse bitter and fearful of the arrival of the future gave in and made one film. It was called *Ashes*. Then in 1924 she died, in Pittsburgh.

Loïe Fuller with a list of questions

Once before Loïe Fuller died in Paris in 1928 she consented to meet Thomas Edison.

Edison very excited in the days before that day constantly adjusted his kinetograph.

No one had ever captured Loïe Fuller live on film in her natural habitat.

Edison took off his hat. Edison put his hat back on. Edison straightened his bow tie.

Edison prepared some remarks on perhaps she knew his cousin in Chicago, and how nice it was in Paris in the spring, everyone said.

On the day Loïe Fuller came she had a list of questions about new angles and intensities of light. She was interested in the highest prismatic quality. She was concerned by refractive propensities. She wondered whether someone could please get around to inventing more efficient incandescent plates, these glass thicknesses were warping some of her projecting shades and to tell the truth were so old-fashioned that frankly he ought to be ashamed of himself.

On the day Loïe Fuller met Thomas Edison she left with a large box of bulbs and diagrams.

She left Edison with his hat still on.

She left Edison standing as still as a nineteenth-century photograph in the middle of his laboratory.

As she said to her girlfriend Gab, these men of cinema, they're so damn delicate, you ask them a few little questions and they just freeze solid forever.

Real names

Tristano Somnians was not the real name of Lina Poletti, but she had discovered that there was something about actresses and pseudonyms. If you don't sign your own name they feel that you really understand them.

Sarah Bernhardt was really named Rosine. Nobody absolutely nobody was allowed to call her Rosine. Rosine was in fact the name she gave to tiny live mice before she fed them to her lion cub.

Eleonora Duse resented her birth in a third-class train car, but she didn't mind being called Eleonora, it meant she was essentially Nora the heroine of *A Doll's House*.

After the war Gertrude Stein took to signing her letters always, Gtrde. The war had taken some of the vowels out of everyone, but always she was Gertrude Stein.

Loïe Fuller was born Mary Louise Fuller in a town outside of Chicago called Fullersburg where almost everyone was also named Fuller.
Sometimes she pretended she had a sister.
Later in her life she did have an imitator named Ida Fuller, but that was not a sister.
In the face of her many imitators Loïe Fuller tried to get everyone to call her La Loïe, but her lawyer said it was just not possible to patent the definite article La.

Gab becoming

Gab Sorère was born under another name. She wrenched her life around to become Gab Sorère.

When Gab was fourteen years old she went to the theatre in Paris with her mother. Onstage Loïe Fuller was dancing radiant and stubborn, strong enough to lift forty pounds of fabric in her arms. Gab watched as Loïe Fuller danced her solid self. She was not a song, she was not a swan. She was not a perfumed cloud of the future. She was a woman who had discovered how to gather all the light in a room to her.

When Gab turned eighteen she bought her first worsted wool suit and a jaunty straw boater. She had read Schopenhauer, but still she held out hope that Loïe Fuller might someday walk through the Jardin du Luxembourg on her arm. In general Gab unlike Schopenhauer was optimistic about women and free will. Gab sat out freckling on a park bench for hours writing letters to the distinguished Mlle Fuller, to Loïe, to *ma très chère Lo*.

Before Gab was twenty-one she and Lo were living together in a house with boxes of ideas. Lo was someone who invented forms of light by willing them incandescently into existence. Gab began to experiment with phosphorescent salts. She wanted to find out how things emitted their own light. She wanted to know how someone became herself.

Sarah Bernhardt could have told her. You sit perfectly still in your statuesque self, you never bow your head for anyone, and you keep the wolf in your lap.

Or Eleonora Duse could have told her. You hollow yourself and dissolve, you gasp with your lungs open and what rushes in is the breath of the role you must play, the essence, the Nora of you.

Fregoli found the question strange, *insomma*, a woman becoming herself, frankly, why waste your time?

VII. The Future of Fregoli

Fregoli and the futurists

Filippo Tommaso Marinetti the founder of futurism disliked oil lamps, contemporary theatre, and muddy ditches. He gave as an example of everything that was wrong two cyclists wending their way down a road in 1909 where he was driving. To Marinetti a cyclist was just impeding what he called the divinity of great speed in cars. He hated the verb wending.

Marinetti gave as an example of everything that was right the glory of a car crash and any show starring Fregoli. Marinetti venerated, as he said, the slap and the punch, the roar of brute acceleration, things greased to their maximum, the shock of the dominant law of life as it smashed into someone. He liked the adjectives hygienic and aggressive.

Once when Marinetti was young he declared that he would like to kill Fregoli in a duel.
He told Fregoli to take it as a compliment. A bullet was hygienic and aggressive. To be killed by an object whose speed exceeded your own was in fact an admirable death for a man.

Later Marinetti wrote an article on superior dynamism as demonstrated by Fregoli and drove all the way down to the Teatro Bellini in Napoli to give him a copy.

In the article Marinetti called Fregoli the synthesis of velocity and transformation. He called Fregoli the death of a century of stupid slow plays. He called Fregoli the precursor of the modern art of cinema. In short he called Fregoli a futurist ahead of his time, which was quite an accomplishment considering

that the futurists believed they were already the future themselves.

At the stage door of Teatro Bellini Fregoli embraced Marinetti
and called him my friend F.T. the Divine Driver but steadfastly
refused the offer of a ride back to his hotel.

The futurists and the fascists

A problem with killing your friends in duels and car crashes is that futurism grows lonely.

Therefore the futurists were always looking out for a new figure of change, someone who would not just stand for the future but brandish it. They wanted a man to blazon and signify, to shoot straight into the soft heart of history. They wanted to take the name of someone who would stand for the swift sharp lurch into the next thing.

F.T. Marinetti was very glad to meet Fregoli in Napoli.
Later F.T. Marinetti was very glad to meet Mussolini in Rome. Mussolini was promising to get the trains to run on time at last.
Privately F.T. Marinetti thought that trains on time were worse than boring but this being Italy was prepared for an initial grinding of gears before the future could shoot forward like a bullet into the heavens of infinite engines.

Finally at least the century was speeding up. Finally at last things in Italy would move at the speed they proclaimed.

Frizzo

Frizzo was an imitator of Fregoli who lived between 1901 and 1902. Being a mediocre imitator, he compressed what little he had and used it up all at once.

In 1901 Frizzo became briefly famous when he was thrown into prison in Rome following an affair with a *chanteuse* who was at best not quite fourteen. In a few months he was at liberty again. Frizzo believed in fast forward.

Being an imitator of Fregoli was frantic, heady work. You had to be ready to run through all the reels, to double down, to double up, to sprint for it. You were always careening behind. People would say you were a quick study, but you were more like a shadow thrown hard against a wall, gasping.

As soon as Frizzo was freed, he went down to the Teatro Bellini in Napoli and did as many shows with his Frizzograph as he could before the end of 1902. Then it was over. Frizzo was finished. Even the *chanteuse* who had just turned fifteen had forgotten him.

Frizzo is a first-person verb form in Italian, meaning I burst forth effervescent from the bottle and then fizzle away quickly into nothing.

Fremo

Fremo was also an imitator of Fregoli. He was a bad copy, or the light was always wrong. He was so pale that you could barely see the edges of him.

In 1900 Fremo appeared in a film with the *danseuse* La Belle Otéro who was known for choosing roles that would show off her beautiful dark eyes. Without blinking she became the consort of three kings, two dukes, and the Italian poet who wanted to sleep with Eleonora Duse. Whole new buildings were erected in France so that cupolas might be formed in the shape of her breasts. In this film La Belle Otéro was the Madonna, her eyes as black as the hearts of sunflowers.
Fremo, forgettably, was Christ.

The new century was already filling up with ambitious dark shapely things. Fremo stood next to them, but the light went right through him and he faltered. He feared he was becoming a mere shadow of the imitator he had once been.

Of course Fremo had a Fremograph, but by then no one wanted to see more of Fremo. Everyone was busy and brightly lit. They were catching their trains and getting things invented on time. Wanly Fremo faded from view, or he was still there and no one noticed.

Fremo is also a first-person verb form in Italian, meaning I shudder, I tremble, I shiver as fate overtakes me.

Il treno delle 9,23

The train departing at 9.23 involved eight people.

It was an amorous episode from 1899.

The mother, the daughters, and the lovers were accompanied by a porter, a conductor, a maidservant, and a plume of choking grey smoke. In the opening scene, the porter trundles across the stage with everyone's steamer trunks stacked on his cart.

All of their trunks were marked FRAGILE.

Inside all of their costumes was Fregoli.

What Fregoli liked about the train at 9.23 was that it existed *in partenza*, a train leaving the station. It would lurch forward violently and push its way out into the world. You would hear it shriek its departure, you would see it roiling the clear air with its smoke.

There was no question of quietly defervescing into stillness, of fading away into shadow.

This train would slash the sky with soot. Its name would be known in great cities. It was built for a century of steel and flashbulbs going off like dynamite in your face.

This train was the act of departing with vigour and style.

Its verb was infinitive, to move boldly forward with everyone watching you.

The amorous episode of *Il treno delle 9,23* was a tangle of whispers, mothers, lovers, and luggage. In the last scene the conductor could be heard blowing his whistle impatiently. A white handkerchief was waving urgently from the wings. The bustle of one daughter was showing through a gap in the curtain. Everything labelled FRAGILE

FRAGILE

FRAGILE

FRAGILE

was teetering on the edge of the cart.

An escape by train, Fregoli felt, was the only suitable ending.

But it was still 1899. The train departing at 9.23 was late.

One day as a lion

By 1923 everyone was saying, at last Mussolini would make the trains in Italy run on time.

Mussolini was saying back to everyone, *Meglio vivere un giorno da leone*, better to live one day as a lion than to run around changeable and erratic like those other people. Better to perish on the stone steps of your certainty than to wonder and hesitate. Better to join the swelling ranks of brave men than to be left behind small and spotted on the ground.

To live one day as a lion is to stand up like a straight white column in the centre of Rome. It is to speed forward with the steely resolve of a steam engine. One day as a lion, to live! Or to die! To march, with your arms stiff at your sides, in the company of men! *Forza!*

In those days there were a lot of men marching around Rome in black shirts and big boots. In their pockets were shiny new coins inscribed *Meglio vivere un giorno da leone*. They had chosen their animal, and no one was going to change their minds about it.

Fregoli asked his friend F.T. Marinetti if this might be the moment when the future finally arrived in Italy. Even if a lion couldn't go as fast as a modern motor car, Marinetti said, it was better than nothing.

Returning to Rome

On the last page of his memoir Fregoli wrote, Every year, in the winter, I return again briefly to Rome, my Rome, and every time I find it more beautiful than before, every time I see it more transformed by the will of our great leader Il Duce Mussolini, and in the face of a transformation so miraculous I myself seem *piccino piccino*, as small as a little boy, but also even more proud to be a Roman.

Romolo who had at last gone home to Rome in 1913 when his mother was dying had always mistrusted the fascists.

Eh, Fre', I'm telling you, Romolo said to Fregoli with a hand serious on his shoulder, these fascists, it's not a game, this one. *È una brutta storia.* How long have I known you, eh, Fre', since you were *piccino piccino*, so listen to me now, you can't become one of them.

Fregoli twisted away from the hand and only for an instant in the doorway turned to make a light bitter bow.

Eh Fre', Romolo said in a voice like a sigh, slamming his suitcase shut on the bed.

Then Romolo got on a train bound for Roma Termini running two hours late and when he got to Rome stopped answering letters.

In those days in Rome no one drank wolf milk anymore. Now it was all organized into pasteurizing machines, hygienic and aggressive. With all of the steam and pistons firing, everyone said, the sparks and the sterilizing, really this was the future. Romolo would drink the milk that tasted like metal vats, but he refused to watch the fascists marching through the *quartiere* in their big boots, renaming things.

È una brutta storia means it is a bad story, it is an ugly history, this is the sad part, don't watch.

L'illustrazione fascista

In 1925 a certain general named Filareti published a pamphlet called *In the Margin of Fascism*.

In his pamphlet General Filareti called Fregoli the greatest artist to represent our time. In his pamphlet the General said spectacles of coloured lights were all very well for a simple populace of the past, but now we must transform Italy into the miraculous future. In short the General called Fregoli a fascist ahead of his time, and Fregoli took it as a complement.

In fact Fregoli had the pamphlet framed and hung in his hall-way.

Shortly thereafter Fregoli appeared in an issue of *L'illustrazione fascista*, a pipe in his teeth, squinting into the sun, his right arm raised stiffly in the fascist salute.
L'ultima trasformazione di un trasformista celebre, the caption read, *Fregoli fascista*.
The latest transformation of a man famous for transforming, Fregoli the fascist.
Fregoli the illustration of fascism.

VIII. Fregoli in Eden

Marinetti moves forward

By 1925 Mussolini made sure that the trains for foreigners and journalists were running right on time. Right on time the trains would depart from Milano, and right on time they would arrive in Rome, stopping for no one. In fact Italians could stand on the platforms of their local stations and see the trains thundering by them at great speeds.

Among them stood Fregoli, bewildered. There he was on the platform *in partenza*, and yet there was no train for him. He resolved to ask Marinetti. The future was making strange movements as it rushed forward, sweeping things aside in its swift wake. It was not making regular stops. Surely Marinetti would explain.

But Marinetti, crazed with joy by the new *autostrada* from Milano to Varese, was always out on inexorable rampages in his motor car. Mad new manifestos issued from him weekly. First it was setting fire to every gondola in Venezia, then it was abolishing pasta because it made Italians sleepy and comfortable.

Soon Marinetti was proclaiming that everyone should prepare to wage rapacious war on virgin lands. Quickly Mussolini declared war on Abyssinia so that everyone would have somewhere to go wage war on.

Marinetti didn't know where Abyssinia was, or that it wasn't called Abyssinia anymore. But he knew how to shout, *A chi l'Abissinia? A noi!* He harried a number of poets into joining the platoon that would invade Addis Ababa. He extolled the use of poison gas on the people who lived there. In fact Marinetti volunteered to go down and show them how to do it himself, hygienic and aggressive, so that there weren't any slow soft survivors left over afterward.

A chi l'Abissinia? means, whose Abyssinia?
Whose Abyssina was that?
Yes well, *una brutta storia,* Abyssinia, that was an ugly scene, those were dark stories, that was a bad bit of history unspooling there, wherever that was, in those days, the futurists, the fascists, the twenties, the thirties, the forties, the sort of things they used to do to people in the name of the nation.
A noi means, it is ours.

Un intervallo

One day Fregoli stopped.

He felt flat, airless, shaken, tremulous. Everything was moving so quickly now. There was so much senseless speeding toward the future. The future in turn was blasting things into incomprehensible shards, now they were going to destroy Roma Termini and rebuild it again as some squat grey stone monolith, the soldiers were off again to the Red Sea, this manifesto to abolish pasta.

Suddenly, urgently, what Fregoli wanted was an intermission, *un intervallo.* At long last he would like an afternoon to sit in the garden and play cards, a week when you didn't have to run around pretending to be other people. He was tired of screeching trains and soldiers shouting everywhere about lions and death. Let them go off to the colonies, let them bloody some faces he didn't have to look at. For his part, Fregoli was ready finally for collodion slowness and comfortable shoes. For the first time he longed to just sit still.

Let other men shave every day and stand for the future.

If they wanted him back, the futurists, the fascists, they could send him a postcard.
After all, now they ran the post office.
Also the radio, the newspapers, the police, the trains, the poets, and every theatre in Livorno including the old Eden.

Fregoli n° 2: Ermete Novelli legge il giornale and *Fregoli n° 7: Sogno nuovo*

In the centre of almost every film Fregoli ever made was Fregoli.

But once Fregoli made two films of the famous actor Ermete Novelli.

Fregoli adored famous actors named Ermete.

Fregoli could watch Ermete Novelli for hours, entranced.

Fregoli could watch his beloved Ermete Novelli read the newspaper.

In fact Fregoli made a film in which Ermete Novelli just reads the newspaper.

The film was called *Ermete Novelli reads the newspaper*.

After that Fregoli made a film in which Ermete Novelli just sits in his garden. Nothing happens. There are some pine trees. There is a dog. It is a slow afternoon in late spring.

Ermete Novelli goes on smiling at nothing in his garden until the film runs out.

Fregoli called this film *Sogno nuovo, A new dream*.

When his beloved Ermete Novelli died in 1919, Fregoli didn't know what to do with himself. For a week he was so aimless and distraught that he could barely read the newspaper.

Then he met the famous actor Ermete Zacconi, who had a beach house in Viareggio.

A new dream.

Fregoli in Viareggio

With that Fregoli sold all of the scenery and three tons of costumes to a man in Genova. He kept only a few dresses in the old steamer trunks, their wooden corners cracking now into splinters, and some letters from the Divine Sarah. It was still early spring, and he felt the cold clotting his bones.

Fregoli left Rome where they were busy smashing Roma Termini into bits and bisecting the city with the grand lines of new streets. Where there had been fish markets, ruins, impoverished families, cemeteries, the *quartiere* of the Jews, warrens of streets twisting together, now there would be broad flat avenues that led straight from one place to another. It was very flat, the future, straight and flat and good for modern motor cars.

Fregoli drove out to Viareggio where the sea stretched out under the sky.
Nothing at all was happening in Viareggio.
People sat on their terraces and closed their eyes in the sunshine. His friend Ermete Zacconi said it was a disgrace, you could hardly get cigarettes on a Sunday, half the time the morning papers didn't come until the afternoon, it was so quiet even the boats in the harbour got bored.

Fregoli bought a house there and called it Eden.

The men of cinema in their gardens

When the men of cinema retire they sit in their gardens like Ermete Novelli and read the morning papers. They look at the pictures of actresses and remark how they are getting old. The Divine Sarah with one leg gone. How fat Loïe Fuller has got. Lithe little Teresina Negri from Torino, such a butterfly when she was a girl, you would never know it now.

The retired men of cinema also go to the gardens of other men of cinema. For example Fregoli often visited his dear friend the famous actor Ermete Zacconi under the palms of his garden.
As it turned out Viareggio was a minor paradise of famous actors named Ermete.
Fregoli in his retirement enjoyed them all.

On nice evenings, a white carnation in his buttonhole, Fregoli would walk up and down the *lungomare* of Viareggio with Ermete Zacconi. Ermete Zacconi was a florid man who had been a tragic actor, and Fregoli liked a good tragedy now and then.

From the terrace of his house on the corner of via Roma, Fregoli could see the calm changeless surface of the sea. On the mornings when he was fortunate to have his dear Ermete Zacconi as a guest, Fregoli would have little coffees served on the terrace with the papers. Against the bright flat backdrop of the sea they would hold up the morning papers, showing each other the pictures of actresses getting old.

Comfortably all afternoon in their gardens the men of cinema
cheated each other at cards.

Fregoli in 1936

In 1936 Fregoli published his memoir.

His favourite story was of the evening long ago when he had
fainted blondly before his father. He loved the tears of that girl
who had been left pregnant by that scamp of a son, *che cretino*,
who couldn't act his way out of a hole in the wall.
Ebbene, babbo! Fregoli says triumphantly to his father at the
end, eh, Papa, well then!
His father had been dead for decades, but Fregoli kept telling
the story in the present tense.
It was 1936 but with a splinter of 1886 stuck in it.
Fregoli still had the nice blue dress.

In 1936 one afternoon Fregoli had lunch on his terrace in
Viareggio with a new young friend named Gino. Gino was a
striking man with a vigorous moustache who wasn't afraid to
say he was an actor of both stage and cinema. At last it was
1936 and you could say things like that. After lunch Gino left
Fregoli in an armchair on the terrace reading the papers, a silhouette limned with the bright flat light of the sea.

In 1936 in the evening Gino came back, and Fregoli was still
there in the same place, immobile, reading the morning papers
although the light was gone and the sea was a dark hush,
and Gino saw him unchanged and knew right away. He went
downstairs to write a telegram express to the best *fioraio* in
Rome, saying send a last white carnation for the buttonhole of
Fregoli, the great Fregoli *il camaleonte*, and do it as fast as possible.

IX. Velia Remaining

Velia sewing

Really the only remaining question is what did Velia think?

Fregoli for decades was coming and going in a great blur of *andirivieni* with Romolo watching him. As soon as they left Rio de Janeiro there was Madrid, and as soon as they left Madrid there was New York to go to. They were crossing whole continents to make their entrances. Hardly had the trunks arrived at Roma Termini heralded by a screech of smoke than they were off again by steamship, wigs piled upon wigs.

Meanwhile Velia was remaining.
She was the remaining question.
When Fregoli left, Velia stayed home not thinking about sewing.
Sewing was just a way of appearing in the world to be doing something useful. Sewing was a front.
Velia began to have questions of her own.

Velia remaining one summer respectably with an aunt on the coast of her childhood went bathing in the sea again after so many years. At last, to swim again in the Bay of La Spezia where Shelley had drowned.
It was nearly the end of the century by then, but the sea was the same.
Idly on a rock Velia wondered how many husbands went sailing off while how many of their wives stayed home accomplishing things and disguising them as embroidery.

Velia had a hatbox where she kept her sewing. It had a false bottom.

Fregoli n° 9: Bagni di mare fine di secolo

Fregoli once made a film called *Bathing in the sea at the end of the century*. Besides the films Fregoli made of his beloved Ermete Novelli it is the only film that does not have Fregoli in it. No one knows why he made it.

It begins with a boating scene of general chaos. There are men falling out of wooden rowboats everywhere and scrambling haplessly to get back into them. Of course they are rocking the boats terribly, and there is only one person who has not fallen into the sea.

The woman who has not yet fallen into the sea clutches at the edge of the wooden boat. She tries to remain calm and to think. In this heavy gown she will be immediately sodden, the sea will swallow her whole and eat her bones for nothing. She must think. She must think about what it takes not to fall overboard. She must think about not drowning. Around her in the water the men are laughing and wringing out their loose shirts and spitting streams of water at each other.

All around her, men are laughing as if this were some kind of marvellous joke.
As if this were a film and not her life rocking violently back and forth.

It is possible that Fregoli made this film for Velia.

Santa Maria in Via

Velia walked through the old *quartiere* considering Fregoli.
Fregoli who had been born very short in 1867 and then become ever more Fregoli, in fact many more Fregolis.
Fregoli expanding outwards, straining the seams of one person.
Fregoli faster and shinier, Fregoli his name blaring in lights, Fregoli a substance so heavy and diffuse that he could take up the space of himself and a hundred others and Velia too.

Some days Velia was only keeping herself in the dark few inches at the bottom of her hatbox.

At that time in Rome the father of Fregoli was dying, and Velia went into a church to light a candle. The church of the *quartiere* was called Santa Maria in Via, and its stone wall formed one side of a dark street where impoverished families crowded the lower floors with their children. Having been in the same place for nearly a thousand years the church Santa Maria in Via was by now indifferent to the deaths of fathers and the births of impoverished children. It was all the same melted wax and women kneeling on cold floors.

Along the street, scraped out of the wall of the church, was a hole that had been there since the sixteenth century.
The hole said: *questa la buca delle zitelle.*
This is the hole of the unmarried women.
It was remarkable, Velia thought kneeling, that the unmarried

women of Rome had been stuck in the same hole for four centuries.

Then she went home to pack everything in crates labelled
FREGOLI
FREGOLI
FREGOLI
FREGOLI. In a week the furniture was ready to be moved to a villa in Asti named Velia.

A wife by train

At the end of the week Velia left Roma Termini for Asti with her hatbox and some blood oranges done up in a handker-chief.

The train was two hours late by itself, and another hour of de-lay was added by the fascists who had decided to destroy the station and build it again from scratch. Grey walls were rising already. Men were pounding their metal hammers on the rub-ble of old stone.

Velia thought that she herself might be changing very quietly, but she could scarcely hear it under the shouting and the hammers. She could barely hear herself at all these days with Fregoli so loudly banging the doors shut. Rushing forward into the future with all of his buttons shining in the sun. The wind blowing back was banging the door shut on everyone who was not rushing forward with him. Marinetti, Mussolini, General Filateli, that poet who was in love with Eleonora Duse, what was his name, who wrote plays for her until she slept with him, D'Annunzio, yes, they were all a blur together dashing at the future.

Velia knew what everyone said of course, he would make the trains run on time.
But the delay in trains is a trick.
With a late train in Italy no one can blame you. You can think by yourself for three hours and emerge as innocent as a virgin saint in a white dress with lace round the hems.

Velia delayed somewhere outside of Pavia peeled a blood orange and settled back in her seat.

Velia the *sarta*

When Velia was young she was told that the *sarta* was a future for honest girls. *Mani all'ago, cuore onesto!* Needle in the hands, honesty in the heart!

Placed in the Teatro Eden of Livorno under an old *sarta* named Lenuccia who had mended, as she would say, more costumes than there were sardines in the sea, Velia learned to whipstitch.
A whipstitch is the fastest form of sewing.
It is much used in theatre because if an actor has three seconds in the wings you can whipstitch half his costume.
Velia a diligent *sarta* learned to whipstitch a man into a costume in two and a half seconds.

Thus when Fregoli met her she could sew, and he married her. Thereafter she was known not as Velia the *sarta* of the Eden but as a Fregoli, *la signora* Fregoli.

Signora Fregoli was also the name of one of the imitators of Fregoli. Fregoli who was not generally fond of his imitators found Signora Fregoli a marvellous joke.

Lenuccia and the heroes

Lenuccia had seen every tragedy to come through the Eden in thirty years. She had seen men fall on their glinting foil swords, and she had seen women screaming through paper streets crying doom, doom is upon us, the fall of the city, the wrath of the gods, alas the sky above is red with bloodlight.

Who d'you think mended their underthings? Lenuccia demanded of Velia.
Or did you think they went around bare as babes under their armour, you naughty girl?

Velia stood in the wings all through the next tragedy at the Eden, watching the actors strain the seams of their costumes. She considered in fact that a *sarta* depended upon all past *sarte*, stretching back to the first *sarta* who had ever made a weak seam. Everything eventually ripped at the weakest seam, and there you were with an eternity of mending.

As it turned out Lenuccia was right.
This man Achille or Ettore or Patroclo or whoever he was, all their armour looked alike, had gashed his sleeve in the second scene and clanking backstage extended his arm to Velia imperiously as if she had been waiting since the dawn of time quiet in the wings just to whipstitch it for him.

Villa Velia

The villa in Asti was called Velia, but the gates which barred its drive were engraved FREGOLI FREGOLI. They swung open and closed for Fregoli and Romolo arriving and departing again, leaving some torn costumes for her in a basket by the stairs.

When Fregoli found her in the gardens to say farewell again Velia had her sewing in her lap. Fregoli had a white carnation tucked into his lapel. *Addio! Addio!* Romolo with one quick hand latched the gate as they left.

Velia considered that she was now herself but also a house. She was still herself but also a wife. She was herself but also a Fregoli, and not even a real one at that. Now Velia in name was an imitation of the man who had married her.

In this case the trick might be to divide yourself into floors. On the ground floor, the gates clanging FREGOLI FREGOLI and the gardens with their endless beds of white carnations. Then the stairs, guarded by her basket of mending like a lion on the steps of a library. And on the second floor, a cool dim space rarely used, shuttered and musty rooms. No one entertained there, and by all appearances it was as dull as an embroidered antimacassar.

Thus Velia had the second floor all to herself.

Wardrobes

Three tons of things were gone, Fregoli assured her, but it seemed to Velia that every wardrobe was somehow still a mass of dresses. Each spring she straightened them, and each winter she packed the wigs in camphor papers. Fregoli still had his very first dress. It was blue, a nice dress, but so threadbare that it was more like a pale blue cloud held together by patches of thread.

When Velia first opened a wardrobe she surveyed the state of the dresses. What mood hung about them, had they been neglected, did they suffer?

In one trunk overlooked for a decade the moths had decimated even the scraps of a lace mask.
Velia was made to atone for this.

One spring, opening the doors of a wardrobe, Velia considered how patient the dresses had been all year. How they hung there empty and neglected, and yet did not seem to have suffered. What was the general mood of dresses kept unused in wardrobes? Were they quiet and content in themselves, withdrawn into the cool dimness of months passing? Or were they so still because a dress pinned to its hanger has already been drained of its life?

Velia in the wardrobe could not help but see limp rows of dead shapes, hanging.

Velia si sveglia

During the war the whole house shook. At night there were flashes of light falling out of the sky and destroying things on the earth below. Fregoli was in Havana or perhaps he was in Paris, the post had slowed to almost nothing, and it was difficult to know anything about the lives of anyone else, only that they were all in the war now.

Idly Velia one night in the cellar was considering while the house rattled above her.
Velia was close to *veglia*, a vigil.
Velia could be a fanciful form of *velo*, a veil, or of *vela*, a sail.
Velia rhymed with *sveglia*, awake, woken up, alert, aware.
Velia si sveglia, Velia awakes, Velia wakes herself up.
Velia è si sveglia, Velia is quite aware.

In Italian the initial *s* can be privative for a verb, or it can be something else. Privative verbs include *sformare*, *sdegnare*, *sfasciare*, to deform, to disdain, to destroy. *Svegliare* is a questionable privative. How can you awaken someone who is already in a state of vigil? How can you become more aware when you have already been watching for years, vigilant, quiet in the wings, your sewing in your lap?

A veil, a sail, Velia at two in the morning considering.

Finale Ligure

From Viareggio you could take the train to La Spezia, and from La Spezia to Genova, and then from the Stazione Genova Principe the train ran slowly along the coast of Liguria stopping everywhere. Beyond Genova was a town called Finale Ligure that existed only between the train tracks and the sea. Some few residents lived there peaceably all year round, and then in the summers all the summer people came from Milano with their beach chairs and cigarettes.

Velia respectably *en route* to the house of an aunt used to hope that the train would linger forever at the little station of Finale Ligure called *Finalmarina*, the end of the sea.

Velia remembered sitting by the window watching the train throw its shadow on the sea, and how the sea glinting would carry that shadow onward at the pace of the train, and for a moment everything was stitched together, the window frame and the waves, the little square of light travelling over the water with the shadow of her own silhouette hollowed out of it. Then she could see the outline of herself moving, the exact space of darkness that was Velia before she arrived at Finalmarina.

Velia in 1936

In 1936 Gino came downstairs and told her.
Velia bowed her head over sewing the last tiny seam in the best suit of Fregoli.
A life, then.
A life in all its chameleons, everyone watching while it changes.

Velia finished the seam and bit off the remaining thread in her teeth as *sarte* have done since time immemorial. Then she went upstairs.

Velia disappears

At first telegrams came to Velia from all of Italy. The condolences, the loss of a hero of our nation, the sincere sympathies, the man who was the magic of cinema before cinema itself existed, an emblem of the future, in homage please accept.

Then telegrams came to Velia from all over the world. In Rio de Janeiro one evening the trams would sit dark in silent tribute. In Paris at the Théâtre Sarah Bernhardt would be his name blazing in lights FREGOLI FREGOLI all across the marquee. In New York a plaque engraved by the Sons of Italy and in Lisbon a likeness in plaster.

The papers of Fregoli were to be consigned to a library in Rome. There were reviews punctiliously cut from decades of newspapers, portraits and picture postcards, letters from the Divine Sarah during the war. There was one vague image of Velia in the gardens and one of Romolo, somewhat in shadow, sitting at a table with Fregoli and some other men no one knew who.

Velia answered the telegrams and expressed the gratitude of Signora Fregoli for all condolences, sympathies, and homages received. She gathered up the papers into boxes marked FREGOLI FREGOLI and sent them off to the Biblioteca in Rome.

Then she disappeared.

The forwarding address of Signora Fregoli

Actually it was known around Viareggio that the Signora Fregoli had sold the house on the corner of Via Roma with its terrace, poor woman, of course she couldn't stay there after, you can only imagine, even though it wasn't her that found him, still, *poveretta*, hadn't they been married since she was just a girl, the shock, the terrible shock well of course she was just shattered and sold it, didn't you hear yet she's moving to a town near Ferrara, the Signora Fregoli is, yes well I'm telling you now, Monettirolo it's called, all in black the widow Fregoli like a proper lady, well as I was saying she put all of her furniture in boxes and had them sent on ahead of her, I saw them go off myself, next month they're saying, just getting the papers tidied now, yes, Monettirolo, nice little town, I'm sure they'll look after her there.

Velia changing

The man at the desk of the hotel in Finale Ligure scarcely looked up at her.

Cognome? he asked.

Sveglia, said Velia, la Signora Sveglia.

He wrote it down as if it were nothing, no question at all, and gave her the key to a room on the second floor.

Velia went upstairs and closing the door behind her became something not Fregoli no one knows what.

BIBLIOGRAPHY

Albright, Ann Cooper. *Traces of Light: Absence and Presence in the Work of Loïe Fuller*. Middletown, CT: Wesleyan University Press, 2007.

Albright, Ann Cooper. "Resurrecting the Future: Body, Image, and Technology in the Work of Loïe Fuller," in *The Oxford Handbook of Screendance Studies*. Ed. Douglas Rosenberg. New York: Oxford University Press, 2016: 715–730.

Aleramo, Sibilla. *Lettere d'amore a Lina*. Ed. Alessandra Cenni. Milano: Savelli, 1982.

"Archivio Film." Archival film collection of the Centro Sperimentale di Cinematografia/Cineteca Nazionale, Rome. http://www.fondazionecsc.it/.

Aubert, Michelle, and Jean-Claude Seguin. *La Production Cinématographique des Frères Lumière*. Paris: Bibliothèque du Film, 1996.

Barnouw, Erik. *The Magician and the Cinema*. New York: Oxford University Press, 1981.

Barrera, Giulia. "Sex, Citizenship and the State: The Construction of the Public and Private Spheres in Colonial Eritrea." In *Gender, Family and Sexuality: The Private Sphere in Italy, 1860–1945*. Ed. Perry Willson. New York: Palgrave Macmillan, 2004: 157–172.

Bernadini, Aldo. *Cinema muto italiano*, vol 1, *Ambiente spettacoli e spettatori 1896–1904*. Ed. Michele Canosa. Bari: Editori Laterza, 1980.

Bernadini, Aldo. "Leopoldo Fregoli, 'cinematografista.'" In *A nuova luce : cinema muto italiano 1 : atti del convegno internazionale, Bologna, 12–13 novembre 1999*. Ed. Michele Canosa. Bologna: CLUEB, 2000: 181–187.

Benadusi, Lorenzo, Paolo Bernadini, and Paola Guazzo. "Introduction: In the Shadow of J.J. Winckelmann: Homosexuality in the Italy During the Long Nineteenth Century." In *Homosexuality in Italian Literature, Society, and Culture, 1789–1919*. Ed Lorenzo Benadusi et al. Newcastle upon Tyne: Cambridge Scholars Publishing, 2017: 1–28.

Bertolo, Luigi. "Fregoli svela i trucchi di Fregoli." *RC: Rivista del cinematografo e delle comunicazione sociali: cinema, teatro, television, radio, pubblicità, informazione*. LXV.1 (1995): 33.

Blom, Ivo. "All the same or strategies of difference: Early Italian comedy in international perspective," in *Italian Silent Cinema: A Reader*. Ed. Giorgio Bertellini. New Barnet: John Libbey, 2013: 171–184.

Body Stages: The Metamorphosis of Loïe Fuller. La Casa Encendida, Madrid. Milano: Skira, 2014.

Brachetti, Arturo, ed. *Fregoli raccontato da Fregoli: le memorie del mago del trasformismo*. Florence: Florence Art Edizioni, 2007.

Brunetta, Gian Piero. *Storia del cinema italiano: 1895–1929*. Roma: Editori Riuniti, 1993.

Burns, Edward M, and Ulla E. Dydo with William Rice, eds. *The Letters of Gertrude Stein & Thornton Wilder*. New Haven: Yale University Press, 1996.

Calle, Sophie. *True Stories*. Arles: Actes Sud, 2016.

Carson, Anne. *Short Talks*. London, Ontario: Brick Books, 1992.

Carson, Anne. *The Albertine Workout*. New York: New Directions, 2014.

Cenni, Alessandra. *Gli occhi eroici: Sibilla Aleramo, Eleonora Duse, Cordula Poletti: una storia d'amore nell'Italia della Belle Époque*. Milano: Mursia, 2011.

Coffman, Elizabeth. "Women in Motion: Loïe Fuller and the 'Interpenetration' of Art and Science." *Camera Obscura* 17.1 (2002): 73–105.

Colagreco, Luigi. "Il cinema negli spettacoli di Leopoldo Fregoli." *Biano & Nero – Bimestrale della Scuola Nazionale del Cinema* 3–4 (2002): 40–59.

Corsi, Mario. "Fregoli pioniere del muto e precursore del sonoro." *Cinema* (Rome) 11 (1936): 416–417.

Croft, Clare, ed. *Queer Dance: Makings and Meanings*. New York: Oxford University Press, 2017.

Dal Maso, Cinzia. "L'antica via del Mortaro nel rione Trevi." *Specchio Romano*. May 2004. http://www.specchioromano.it/fondamentali/Lespigolature/2004/Maggio/L'anticaviadelMortaronelrioneTrevi.htm.

De Céspedes, Alba. *Dalla parte di lei*. Milano: Mondadori, 1957.

Farfan, Penny. "Fairy of Light: Performative Ghosting and the Queer Uncanny." In *Performing Queer Modernism*. Oxford: Oxford Scholarship Online, 2017.

Ferrante, Elena. *La frantumaglia*. Roma: Edizioni e/o, 2003.

Forgione, Nancy. "'The Shadow Only': Shadow and Silhouette in Late Nineteenth-Century Paris." *The Art Bulletin* 81.3 (1999): 490–512.

Fregoli, Leopoldo. "Memorie della mia vita." *Scenario* (Rome) 6–12 (1934), 1–5 (1935).

Fuller, Loïe. "Gab." Folder 22, Loie Fuller Papers (unpublished). Dance Collection, The New York Public Library. Astor, Lenox and Tilden Foundations. 1892.

Fuller, Loïe. *Fifteen Years of a Dancer's Life: With Some Account of Her Distinguished Friends*. Boston: Small and Maynard, 1913.

Galasso, Catherine. *Bring on the Lumière!* Performance. 11 Nov 2011. ODC Theater, San Francisco. Performances by Marina Fukushima and Christine Bonansea.

Garelick, Rhonda K. *Electric Salome: Loie Fuller's Performance of Modernism*. Princeton, NJ: Princeton University Press, 2007.

Garelick, Rhonda K. "Setting the Air on Fire: Loïe Fuller and the Task of 'New Biography.'" Proceedings of the Society of Dance History Scholars 31st Annual Conference, June 12–15, Skidmore College, Saratoga Springs, NY. 2008: 198–202.

Gaudreault, André. "From 'Primitive Cinema' to 'Kine-Attractography,'" in *Cinema of Attractions Reloaded*. Ed. Wanda Strauven. Amsterdam: University of Amsterdam Press, 2006: 85–104.

Gunning, Tom. "The cinema of attractions: Early film, its spectators, and the avant-garde," in *Early Cinema: Space, Frame, Narrative*. Ed Thomas Elsaesser. London: BFI, 1991: 56–62.

Gunning, Tom. "Loïe Fuller and the Art of Motion: Body, Light, Electricity and the Origins of Cinema," in *Camera Obscura, Camera Lucida: Essays in Honor of Annette Michelson*. Ed. Richard Allen and Malcolm Turvey. Amsterdam: Amsterdam University Press, 2003. 75–90.

Guzzi, Paolo. *Café-chantant a Roma: Il Caffè-concerto tra canzoni e «varietà» da Lina Cavalieri alla Bella Otero, da Fregoli a Petrolini*. Roma: Rendina Editore, 1995.

Hornby, Louise. *Still Modernism: Photography, Literature, Film*. New York: Oxford University Press, 2017.

Ialongo, Ernest. "Filippo Tommaso Marinetti: the Futurist as Fascist, 1929–37." *Journal of Modern Italian Studies*, 18.4 (2013): 393–418.

Jarro [Giulio Piccini]. *Pagine allegre*. 4th edition. Firenze: R. Bemporad e figlio, 1904.

Kraut, Anthea. *Choreographing copyright : race, gender, and intellectual property rights in American dance*. New York: Oxford University Press, 2015.

Latimer, Tirza True. *Women Together/Women Apart: Portraits of Lesbian Paris*. New Brunswick, NJ: Rutgers University Press, 2005.

Lento, Mattia. *La scoperta dell'attore cinematografico in Europa*. Pisa: Edizioni ETS, 2017.

Letamendi, Jon, and Jean-Claude Seguin Vergara. "Leopoldo Fregoli." Le GRImh [Groupe de Réflexion sur l'Image dans le monde hispanique]. 2015. https://www.grimh.org/index.php?option=com_content&view=article& layout=edit&id=1159&lang=fr#1

Lista, Giovanni. *Loïe Fuller et ses imatrices*. Film. Produced by the Cinémateque de la danse (1994); second expanded version produced by CNRS, Paris (2006).

Lista, Giovanni. *Loïe Fuller: Danseuse de la Belle Époque*. Paris: Hermann Danse, 2007.

The Lumière Project: The European Film Archives at the Crossroads. Ed. Catherine A. Surowiec for Projecto Lumière. Lisbon: Associação Projecto Lumière, 1996.

Mannoni, Laurent. *The Great Art of Light and Shadow: Archeology of the Cinema*. Translated and edited by Richard Crangle. Exeter: University of Exeter Press, 2000.

McCarren, Felicia. *Dancing Machines: Choreographies of the Age of Mechanical Reproduction*. California: Stanford University Press, 2003.

Mercatali, Oscar. FREGOLI: *Da Caffè-Concerto al Teatro: Note, Appunti e Aneddoti*. Roma: Edoardo Perino, 1893.

Milletti, Nerina e Luisa Passerini, eds. *Fuori della norma: Storie lesbiche nell'Italia della prima metà del Novecento*. Torino: Rosenberg & Sellier, 2007.

Nohain, Jean, and François Caradec. *Fregoli (1867–1936): sa vie et ses secrets*. Paris: La Jeune Parque, 1968.

North, Dan. "Magic and Illusion in Early Cinema." *Studies in French Cinema* 1.2 (2001): 70–79.

Parfitt, Claire. "Like a butterfly under glass": the cancan, Loïe Fuller and cinema." *International Journal of Performance Arts and Digital Media* 5.2–3 (2009): 107–120.

Pellegrini, Glauco. "Fregoli ou Le premier 'appareil' de projection sonore." *La Revue du Cinéma* 3.14 (1948): 48–51.

Polezzi, Loredana. "White, Male, and Italian?: Performing Masculinity in Italian Travel Writing about Africa," in *In Corpore: Bodies in Post-Unification Italy*. Ed. Loredana Polezzi and Charlotte Ross. Cranbury, NJ: Rosemont Publishing, 2007: 29–55.

Potter, Susan Margaret. "Queer Timing: The Emergence of Lesbian Representation in Early Cinema." Diss. University of Auckland, 2012.

Pruska-Oldenhof, Izabella. "Loïe Fuller's Serpentines and Poetics of Self-Abnegation in the Era of Electrotechnics," in *The Oxford Handbook of Screendance Studies*. Ed. Douglas Rosenberg. New York: Oxford University Press, 2016: 45–62.

Rambaud, Patrick. *Les mirabolantes aventures de Fregoli*. Paris: Editions François Bourin, 1991.

Ross, Charlottte. *Eccentricity and Sameness: Discourses on Lesbianism and Desire between Women in Italy, 1860s–1930s*. Bern: Peter Lang, 2015.

Rusconi, Alex. *Fregoli: la biografia*. Roma: Stampa alternativa/Nuovi equilibri, 2011.

Sainati, Augusto. "La personnalisation du Cinématographe: Fregoli et son 'Fregoligraph," in *L'aventure du Cinématographe, actes du Congrès mondial Lumière*. Lyon: Aléas, 1999: 181–185.

Schettini, Laura. *Il gioco delle parti: Travestimenti e pauri sociali tra Otto e Novecento*. Milano: Mondadori, 2011.

Schwartz, Selby Wynn. "Light, Shadow, Screendance: Catherine Galasso's *Bring on the Lumière!*" in *The Oxford Handbook of Screendance Studies*. Ed. Douglas Rosenberg. New York: Oxford University Press, 2016: 205–224.

Seguin, Jean-Claude. "Frégoli et le «frégolisme» (XIXe–XXe)." In *Travestir au Siècle d'Or et aux XXe–XXIe siècles: regards transgénériques et transhistoriques.* Ed. Natalie Dartai-Maranzana et Emmanuel Marigno. Saint-Étienne: Reboul/Université de Saint-Étienne, 2012: 171–184.

S.L.B. "Behind the Scenes with Fregoli." *The Sketch: An Illustrated Miscellany.* July 20, 1898: 550.

Snorton, C. Riley. "'A New Hope': The Psychic Life of Passing." *Hypatia* 24.3 (2009): 77–92.

Solomon, Matthew. "'Twenty-Five Heads under One Hat,'" in *Meta-morphing: Visual Transformation and the Culture of Quick-Change.* Ed. Vivian Sobchack. Minneapolis: University of Minnesota Press, 2000: 3–20.

Schmalsteig, Manuel. "*Danse serpentine, [I].*" *Catalogue Lumière: L'œuvre cinématographique des frères Lumière.* 2015. https://catalogue-lumiere.com/danse-serpentine-i/.

Solnit, Rebecca. *Motion Studies: Time, Space and Eadweard Muybridge.* London: Bloomsbury, 2003.

Strauven, Wanda. "S/M." In *Mind the Screen: Media Concepts According to Thomas Elsaesser.* Ed. Jaap Kooijman, Patricia Pisters, and Wanda Strauven. Amsterdam: Amsterdam University Press, 2008: 276–287.

Strauven, Wanda. "Futurist Poetics and the Cinematic Imagination: Marinetti's Cinema without Films." In *Futurism and the Technological Imagination.* Ed. Günter Berghaus. Amsterdam and New York: Rodopi, 2009: 201–228.

Tabet, Frédéric. "La transparence du Fregoligraph en question," in *Performing New Media, 1890–1915.* Ed Kaveh Askari et al. New Barnet (UK): John Libbey Publishing Ltd., 2014: 57–66.

Townsend, Julie. *The Choreography of Modernism in France: La Danseuse, 1830–1930.* New York: Routledge, 2010.

Valentini, Valentina. *Teatro in imagine: eventi performativi e nuove media.* Roma: Bulzoni Editore, 1987.

Veroli, Patrizia. "Loie Fuller's Serpentine Dance and Futurism: Electricity, Technological Imagination and the Myth of the Machine." In *Futurism and the Technological Imagination.* Ed. Günter Berghaus. Amsterdam and New York: Rodopi, 2009: 125–148.

Visani, Alessandro. *Genere, identità e razzismo nell'Italia fascista.* Roma: Aracne, 2012.

ACKNOWLEDGEMENTS

I am indebted to Catherine Galasso for the first sparks of this book, which flew out flashing from her dance piece *Bring on the Lumière!*. My research was supported by the staff of the Cineteca Nazionale in Rome, particularly Sergio Bruno and Viridiana Rotondi. In the time of this book becoming itself, I have been held aloft by a wonderful circle: Masha Gutkin, John Hill, Amanda Goldstein, Tom McEnaney, Sima Belmar, Lucile Raux, Monique Jenkinson, Marisa Mandile, Amie Dowling, Julian Carter, Emile DeWeaver, Mesro Coles-El, Siavash Karimzadegan, Stacey Cobalt, Molly Parent, Stephen Sparks, Ida Dominijanni, Sabrina Sanità, Claudio Rosati, Tory Dobrin, Jesús Rodríguez Velasco, and above all my absolutely lovely family. Thanks to David Borrowdale and Reflex Press for their unwavering enthusiasm for the indescribable. And the person who went with me through every single film strip until they spliced at last into a life, is – as always – Michael.

~

The author and publisher wish to thank the editors of *Passages North* who first published 'Il Camaleonte', 'Eden', '*Fregoli nº 1: Fregoli retroscena*', '*Fregoli nº 25: Segreto per vestirsi*', and 'Romolo the *sosia*' as 'The Secret to Dressing Yourself (with Help)', July 2021.

REFLEX PRESS

Reflex Press is an independent publisher based in Abingdon, Oxfordshire, committed to publishing bold and innovative books by emerging authors from across the UK and beyond.

Since our inception in 2018, we have published award-winning short story collections, flash fiction anthologies, and novella-length fiction.

www.reflex.press
@reflexfiction